BOOKS BY *Franklin Russell*

❁❁❁❁❁

ARGEN THE GULL
(1964)

WATCHERS AT THE POND
(1962)

These are Borzoi Books,
published in New York by Alfred A. Knopf

Argen the Gull

ARGEN

THE GULL

BY

Franklin Russell

WITH PHOTOGRAPHS BY THE AUTHOR

McCLELLAND AND STEWART LIMITED

Toronto   Montreal

The Canadian Publishers
McClelland and Stewart Limited
25 Hollinger Road, Toronto 16

One of the most successful members of the world-wide

gull family, Laridae, is the herring gull,

Larus argentatus

Contents

NOTE ON ILLUSTRATIONS

A portfolio of photographs, taken by the author, follows page 114. The photographs are related to the text by means of a special narrative caption.

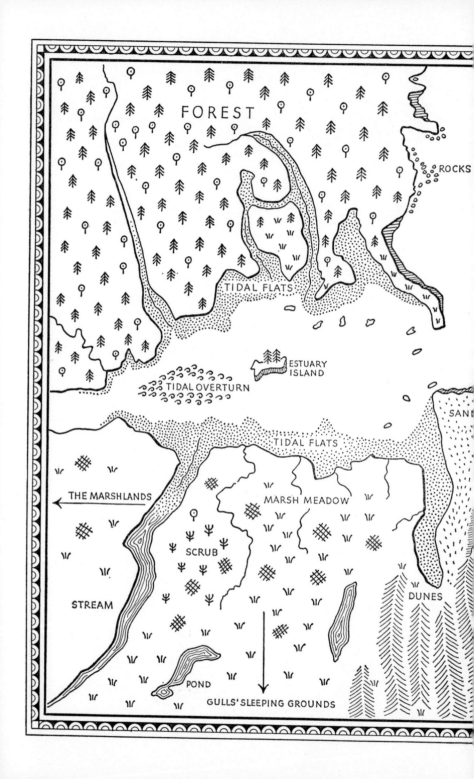

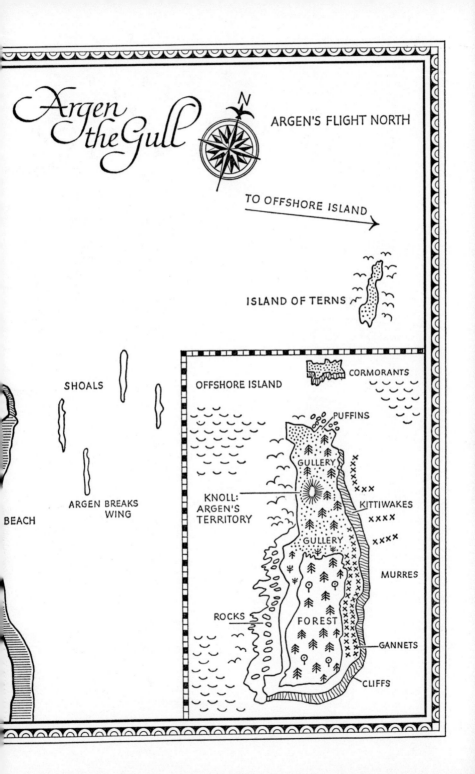

Argen
the Gull

N

ARGEN'S FLIGHT NORTH

TO OFFSHORE ISLAND

ISLAND OF TERNS

SHOALS

OFFSHORE ISLAND

CORMORANTS

PUFFINS

GULLERY

KNOLL:
ARGEN'S
TERRITORY

KITTIWAKES

ARGEN BREAKS
WING

BEACH

GULLERY

MURRES

ROCKS

FOREST

GANNETS

CLIFFS

Argen the Gull

CHAPTER 1

Fantasms in an Ocean Mist

FTER the rain, the wind came briefly, cool and fresh. Behind it, the horizon was muffled in a gray pall. The sea moved under a sickly sun and the day stood at the beginning of a change coming out of the ocean. Sea and shore silently awaited the transmutation. No fin or wing disturbed the amorphous expanse of the shore. Dunelands and marshlands spread darkly away from the yellow light.

The strand was still because it was high tide. The water obscured all the hunting territories and momentarily the tidal currents and overturns that made the sea live were passive. Gulls and terns dozed on sandbanks. A duck floated alone, a speck in the infinite. A seal's head projected from the sea like a black rock. A fox, invisible among bushes of beach plum, yawned and yearned for the night, when he would hunt seabirds.

A solitary gull, appearing out of the south, at last broke the stillness. He flew with distinctive chopping motions of his curved wings, not gracefully but sturdily determined, and he passed undeviatingly over sand and sea. His right wing was bent downward at the elbow and gave him a strangely unbalanced appearance. He ignored a large flock of gulls dozing on a sandbank and flew on as some of them called inquiringly. He disappeared into a yellow blaze of light, emerged, and threw a pale shadow on the colorless sea. Ahead, he could see the last jutting tip of a long sandbar: the end of the land and the beginning of the deepening sea.

As he flew, the horizon darkened. An offshore meeting of two currents, one warm, the other cold, created mist along the line of their collision and it boiled up like steam. It thickened and the gull flew into it. He flew from yellow brilliance into chilly gloom, and he was now well separated from sun and sea and flew in wet silence. Beads of moisture gathered over his nostrils and eyes.

His long, powerful beak, yellow touched with red, reached forward from his sleek white head. His eyes, amber, unblinking, set on each side of his head, gave him monocular vision to each side and binocular vision ahead. His underbody, from throat to fan-shaped tail, was pure white, and his reddish webbed feet were hanging limply below his body as though he were about to land. His wings were pale gray above, heavily tipped with black, and fringed along their trailing edges with white. As they beat, the gull's back and chest heaved and flexed with the movement of powerful actuating muscles. He was a scrap of life in a void, and his exterior form revealed nothing except his color, shape, texture, and activity. His animation was well hidden.

He rode the air on wings driven by food being converted to protoplasm and being exchanged for energy, by the rapid pulsing of a four-chambered heart racing blood through his veins, by air being pulled through his nostrils to purify the blood through a network of vessels and capillaries, by air drawn into large air sacs and into hollow bones.

The energy and hollow buoyancy of this flying creature sent him moving in flight that was fired by the efficiency of his digestion. Earlier in the day, he had smashed and eaten a large mussel, which had passed quickly through his crop—a storage chamber to accommodate sudden large influxes of food—and had become involved in a complex digestive process which, by now, had absorbed most of the flesh of the shellfish and was converting it into blood, protein, acid, and muscle. The unassimilable residue, a small fraction of the original mass, would shortly be expelled into the mist. The smashed shell fragments would move in the opposite direction, back through gut and crop, and be expelled through the gull's mouth.

Outwardly, the gull's flight was as sure as ever. But his sense of balance was faltering. One moment he tended to slip to the right. He corrected this with a strong right wingbeat. But he felt himself veering again, this time to the left. His vision was imperfect and the formless mist flickered with images, perhaps real, more likely illusory. A large seagoing bird banked ahead of him, but the vision changed abruptly and the air moved with the passage of a hundred, a thousand, ten thousand wings. The nameless birds were gone and left only a fading image in the gull's brain. He flew on.

His flight was in the present, but he was part of a long flight through evolution. It had begun millions of years before, when an infinitely more primitive creature, heavy-boned, clumsy, slow-brained, propelled itself forward in a convulsion of effort and rose briefly from the ground, feet dangling, forelimbs stiffly outspread to steady its short glide. Flight, once begun, drew the fliers across forest and sea.

They split up and spread out to exploit the world. Some developed lighter bodies and hollow bones and headed for the sky. Others learned to swim, developed heavy, muscled bodies and shorter wings, and became submarine. In the forest skulked other creatures who learned to fly but then came back to earth to hunt on foot. The gull evolved to swim, to walk, and to fly with almost equal facility.

The mist cleared slightly and the flying gull saw, through rifts, that the water was flecked with foam as the outgoing tide turned over violently. The water whispered in the fog, eerily immediate. The gull saw small fish rising in the overturn. He knew that with them would be many small creatures, shrimp, crab, and larvae, but he ignored them and flew on.

His wings were tiring perceptibly and a slow-burning pain spread across his chest. The illusions returned. A towering wave sent him swerving away. The image of a storm and whitened waves appeared and then vanished. He seemed to be floating high in the air in bright sun, and he heard his mate's last cry and he turned toward her. But the moment passed and only mist surrounded him, empty and opaque. He heard the cry of a falcon; it lingered and was superimposed on the sound of gulls fleeing from an eagle. Dark and foreboding, the sea was silent again. No falcons or eagles were anywhere near him.

The mist was now so dense that the gull flew in subconscious response to his sense of balance and proximity to the water. He had been guided by the last view of the land and by the tide rip, but now he might already be lost. He needed another sign. Innumerable droplets of water continually collected out of the mist onto his wing, back, and tail feathers, drew themselves into drops, and were whipped away. The feathers remained dry and absorbed none of the water. The gull's feathers had, in fact, helped bring his kind to prominence at the shore and their structure showed the scope of evolution.

As the gull beat his wings downward, the primary feathers, the longest, outermost members, rose upward and created a pair of bevel-shaped fans. These drove the bird forward. The motion was so powerful that when the upstroke began, the wings relaxed and, the feathers bending downward, the horizontal motion scarcely diminished. The action of his flight was made possible by the unique structure of the primaries themselves. Each feather was supported by a central tubular shaft from which sprouted several hundred smaller shafts which gave the feather its width. From these, in repetitive fashion, sprouted yet another system of shafts, complexly interconnected with the adjoining shafts by tiny hooks. The result was a flat, thin, air-impervious fan.

The gull's body feathers were equally efficient for the job they had to do. Two complete systems of feathers covered the gull's body. The outer feathers resembled small wing feathers and fitted finely together, giving the bird his compact shape. Beneath these was a downy layer of finer feathers, without hooks to hold them. In flight, they were crushed flat by the outer feathers, which were pulled tightly against the gull's body by muscles in his skin. If he relaxed these muscles, the outer feathers lifted away from the body and the inner, downy feathers instantly sprang up. This hidden layer enabled the gull to stand all night enveloped in sleet or snow, the wind searching his feathers, his body temperature undiminished, protected by the insulating air held in his feathers.

The origin of the feathers was a mystery. They might have come in response to the gull's ancestors' need to fly; or they may have developed primarily to keep the body warm and only later to enable the creature to fly. Somewhere in the gull's ancestral past, the first feathers appeared and crept outward while forelimbs modified into wings and the possibility of flight became reality. Meantime, the great capacity to generate energy was building up inside the feathered body and this eventually provided the power to lift the creature off the ground. The reptilian past faded and the supreme coordination of mental and physical function put the bird into the air.

The mist passed in thick columns. The gull's aerial vertigo disappeared and with it went the illusions. He saw clearly and flew steadily. He was close enough to the gray water to see it spasmodically through rifts in the mist. The steady hiss of disturbed water sounded ahead. Soon he was passing over a familiar curving spit of sand. It was a peninsular projection from a small, flat offshore island which in midyear harbored many seabirds. He was reassured. The sound of sea died away and he faced the open ocean.

The gull's direct and undeviating flight reflected his character. For twenty years, he had ranged along the variegated meeting place of sea and land, offshore islands, saline marshes, dunelands, estuaries, mud flats, rivers, ponds, lagoons, rocky cliffs, and ocean beaches. He was an omnivorous hunter, at once a scavenger, a hunter of birds, fish, insects, carrion, shellfish, and eggs. He knew the strand in minute detail. His comprehension of it verged on intelligence. He knew the times of the tides, the habits of fish, the language of many other birds, the phases of the weather, and he was both diurnal and nocturnal.

His versatile encompassment of sea and shore meant that he lived at many levels. He was one of the few shorebirds who did not retreat from ice and snow. He was not discommoded by high winds or heavy seas; he relished violent weather. In the past, his ancestors had shown this elasticity of spirit by retreating and advancing up and down the strand with the arrival and departure of many ice ages. The herring gulls became generally skillful whereas the rest of the great gull family developed specific skills. Some remained in the Arctic, others became oceanic and remained beyond sight or influence of land for months. Some learned to dive and swim underwater. Others settled inland and never saw the sea. The gulls occupied specialized niches in their ocean-land habitat; the herring gull ranged all over, sharing each of the gull talents in diminished form.

The herring gull was, in fact, an amalgam of all seabirds. He flew well, but his range was small compared with that of the albatross, which might wander over Arctic ice floes in one season and through Antarctic mist in another. He could swim, but his ability was nothing compared with that of the auk family—puffins, dovekies, murres, razorbills, and guillemots—chunky-bodied, short-winged birds who were adapting their powers of flight to become great submarine hunters who hunted like seals and cod for their food. The gull was a traveler, but a timid one compared with the ocean-ranging of the long-winged shearwaters, or the swallow-like petrels, who needed land only to breed. He flew well enough to cross any ocean, but not easily. He could penetrate the surface of the sea, but not deeply.

It was now growing darker. The diffused light of the sun faded. Ahead, the gull heard a hiss of sound, indicating that he was still headed accurately. The sound was the sea breaking around a small outcrop of rocks. In his brief glimpse of the rocks, the gull saw a pair of puffins standing together.

They were lost in the mist and were waiting till it cleared before they returned to their burrows on some nearby island. They turned their brightly colored, conical beaks upward and watched the fleeting form of the silent gull.

Alone in the mist again, the gull sensed the presence of an island ahead, even though he saw nothing. He was now flying surely. The island, the rock, and the slightly brighter appearance of the mist behind him told him his direction and the time of day. To confirm his sense of the presence of the island, odd seabirds appeared in the mist. Three petrels flashed underneath him. A black-backed gull groaned out an unearthly cry nearby. Three crows appeared and disappeared with spectral speed. A guillemot sped low along the water and faded grayly. A small gull, a kittiwake, gave a harsh cry as she swerved from his flight.

The island imposed itself on the gull's senses. Then its massive bulk loomed out of the sea. Tall cliffs echoed every splash of wave or cry of bird. The gull changed his course as he saw the rocky cliffs, and flew parallel to them.

Now, at his shoulder, a panoply of marine birds fled past. The walls of the cliff were decorated with long lines of kittiwakes huddled closely together; they looked like undulating, composite creatures. The gull caught glimpses of startled murres craning lithe necks at him, their beady black eyes glistening in sleek black heads as they flashed past his beating wing and disappeared. A pair of cormorants winged by quickly, and a gannet, white and graceful, passed silently overhead on six-foot wings. A tern, dwarfed by the big bird, flew jerkily beneath the gull.

The proximity of the island flooded the gull's senses with illusive images of cliffs, of high winds blowing against them, and wind currents constantly threatening to drive him against their granitic faces. The rumble of a big sea echoed and seemed to surround him. A cry of danger rang out and the air was filled with fleeing birds. An eagle loomed up and was gone. The cliffs vanished; a dark shoreline appeared; the sea was hushed. The murres were making their run for the sea. Their upright, black-and-white bodies stumbled down the rugged slopes in legions; ten thousand took to the water in one instant and spread out like a stain, swimming and diving exuberantly in their joy to be free of the island. The images continued, incomprehensible and confusing, and the gull flew on unsteadily past the misty cliffs.

He knew the flight must end soon and he was exhausted. His chest burned and his crooked wing ached. The cliffs dodged back and forth. He turned to make a landing, but misjudged his approach and struck rock with his left wing. He spun around sharply and sprawled on a narrow ledge. In response to his clumsy arrival, a group of murres bolted out of a crack in the rocks and flew away into the mist.

The gull righted himself and stood up unsteadily. He looked outward, but his eyes were losing their bright fire of awareness. His senses reeled from the throaty sounds of gannets calling, the buzzing cries of the kittiwakes, and the murmur of the invisible sea far below. The mist became oppressively dark and a feeling of helplessness suffused him. He was now chilled and frightened.

The gull on the ledge was Argen.

CHAPTER 2

The Island

THE first sounds Argen ever heard came to him indistinctly through the shell of the egg in which he was contained. The egg, slightly tapered at one end, lay in a roughly circular nest of dried grasses in an island gullery.

The sounds beyond the egg were muffled cries and scrapings as his egg was moved or bumped against another egg in the nest. He could hear sudden screaming uproars that excited him. In a few days, he would be able to pipe out a thin cry to communicate his presence. Each day his hearing grew more acute, as did all his developing senses. His squirming movements became more vigorous. He heard squeaks, groans, cries of *koy-koy-koy*, whistles, mew calls, shrieks, chuckles, and mutters. But in all this conglomeration of sound, one muted cry would instantly still his squirming and silence his peeping. He had never seen his mother, but he recognized her cry of warning.

The unseen world of the gullery spread all around Argen's egg. The sounds in his ears were the colonial gulls communicating pleasure, anger, watchfulness, hunger, affection, warning, fear, and frustration. Though he was not yet born, the sounds were becoming a part of him as he matured.

Yet, in the egg, Argen was so well sealed off from the outside world that the calls were merely pricks to his immature senses. They entered his tiny brain and he wriggled, perhaps responsively. His body became charged with an urgency to escape from the egg. But these inchoate thrustings lacked conviction and the egg remained intact.

The island sprawled in warmth under an early-summer sun. Long and narrow, it presented lofty gray-black cliffs to the eastern sea. Its surface fell away from the high eastern coast to the low western cliffs. Its varied topography made it a haven for seabirds. Sudden alarms might see the island surmounted by a canopy of wheeling birds.

The herring gulls opportunistically occupied any place where they could build nests, on shingle shores, on rocks, in deep patches of ragweed, and among gloomy spruce thickets. Some even built rough nests in trees. The main concentration of the gulls was at the northern end of the island, where thousands of generations of nesting birds had killed much of the forest and left the land richly clothed in grass and marked by stark upthrust skeletons of dead spruces. Argen's egg nestled here. To the south were spruce woods; to the west, an upflung cliff and more spruce. In this sanctuary, forty thousand gulls nested, their combined numbers a bulwark against their enemies.

The gulls shared the island with many other colonial birds. The eastern side of the island, along the topmost slopes, was blanketed by a gannet colony. It overflowed down the steep, broken cliffs and filled every available flat space among the rocks. On the clifftop slopes, the big birds spread away in massed thousands and each nesting female occupied only enough space to allow her to turn around. The birds at the fringes of the colony nested among the spruces, and their massive presence, like that of the gulls, was steadily killing the forest and pushing it away from the cliffs.

The great size of the gannets—two feet standing height, a wingspan of six feet—and their fearless authority overshadowed the contiguous presence of thirty thousand kittiwakes who nested anywhere along the cliffs where the gannets could not get a foothold. They were a little more than half the size of the herring gulls, and the nesting females crowded together, tail to head, in lines along the cliffs, each bird crouched over a scrap of mud and rubbish that was her nest.

Also occupying the cliffs, but less noticeably, were ten thousand murres, immaculately black and white; penguin-like, they yet flew swiftly, true oceanic birds who were uncomfortable ashore and who, by their alert, tense, watchful stances, seemed anxious to be gone. At the northern end of the cliffs, where rocks had fallen in several massive slides, the growling calls of puffins sounded. These birds resembled murres, but they looked strangely exotic with their powerful, brightly colored bills.

The island was a repository, a moving mosaic of color and sound, constantly dynamic. One moment the gannets would be leaving their cliffside to go planing away over the glistening sea at high speed, then rising into a hovering mass silhouetted against the dawn. The next instant an alarm sent the gulls up from their colony, and their screams hung over the island in a collective voice of concern. The chick Argen stirred uneasily. A tight-knit group of murres appeared in the east in a very low, fast-moving formation. They ignored the other birds, and when close to the cliffs suddenly tilted upward and disappeared into a black slot that was the entrance to one of the murre colonies on the side of the cliff.

The spectacle was continuous. While some colonies relapsed into lethargy, others throbbed with action as fish were brought ashore from successful hunting expeditions. Occasionally, insensate joy gripped the birds and curtains of them hung over the sea around the island. Puffins came cutting through them, preoccupied with purposeful travel and insensitive to the joys of idle flying.

Night did not end the mass noises of the gullery. The entire island was active in the dark. The *koy-koy-koy* cries of the gulls sounded along every invisible horizon, and the clifftops whispered to the *chickerel-chickerel* sound of petrels as they came in cautiously from the sea, small webfooted seabirds whose lives were mysterious, who were breeding in burrows all over the island. Their soft wings fluttered in such lightly sustained flight that they looked more like large swallows than seabirds as they brushed against tall grasses, spruce foliage, and one another, settling and rising from the ground in a flicker of movement only barely revealed in nascent moonlight.

The island slept and wakened rhythmically, and Argen, swathed in embryonic tissue in the mucid interior of the egg, blindly gathered his resources to be born. By now he was possessed by an urge to escape. His beak was tipped with a tiny egg-tooth. Though blind and clumsy, he used this to push and scrape against the shell. The egg moved as he twisted convulsively, and his mother stood erect and looked down curiously. After a day, while his mother was hunting and his father was brooding the egg, Argen broke through the shell. A flood of light struck his membranous eyelids and he paused for a moment, expectant, as his senses registered the alien world. His father stood up and peered closely at the jagged hole in the shell. The life force in Argen drove on. He chipped more shell away from the hole and by evening was ready to free himself. With a lunge, he thrust feet and head hard against the weakened shell. It split and he sprawled beside the other egg. In the dark, his mother returned to the nest, and Argen's last sensation, before sleeping, was the enfolding, drying embrace of her breast feathers as she settled to brood.

Once hatched, Argen grew rapidly. He could see almost immediately, though at first his sight was restricted to impressions of the other egg, mute and still, beside him, the bacteria inside working its contents into putrid liquid. On the morning of his third day of life, he was struck by a brilliant light that burned into his skull. His mother had gone. His father stood near. The early sunlight sprawled across the gullery and shone directly into Argen's eyes. He became frightened at what he saw. The wind waved grasses; gulls flew low overhead. His sight broadened with images over ensuing days. He became aware of redness—of dawns and sunsets, and at the tip of his mother's beak, as she, with writhing neck, regurgitated half-digested scraps of food from her crop. He reached up at this red mark in an agony of hunger, and by pecking at it he procured an instantaneous response in the form of food. Red was symbolical of food and security.

His vision extended beyond the nest and he saw the stark outlines of dead spruces burned blackly against the light of dawn and the shapes of gulls momentarily motionless in them. He stood up in the nest as he saw his mother but then responded to her *ka-ka-ka* alarm call and crouched down instantly, frozen in obedience. But the ragweed around the nesting site did not wholly conceal him, and his crouching was poor protection. On the ninth day of his life the *ka-ka-ka* call sounded as he was dozing. Quickly, he ran from the nest across a patch of rock and into a tussock of grasses. From then on, he used this secondary shelter whenever the alarm sounded.

He soon passed out of this early, vulnerable stage of life— when almost any gull, given the chance, would swallow him in a gulp—into a petulant and arrogant awareness of his new world. By his twentieth day he could recognize his mother visually at great distances from the nest. At the same time, he became exceedingly wary of the world just beyond his clear vision as he grew aware of the scope of the gullery, the sea muttering in the distance, and the wind hissing through the grasses.

His downy covering thickened, and he felt the bite of the sun through it so strongly that he sensed it was dangerous. He learned to stay in the shadow of his parent's body. At first he was able to stand under the tails of the big birds, but he was soon too tall for such refuge and then stood beside his mother and hunched down away from the direct rays of the sun. This was Argen's most sensitive age.

Rain began falling, late one evening, after a series of gusty squalls which blew out of the east. It dropped softly and steadily, and Argen heard it striking the ragweed leaves and pattering on his mother's back feathers. It became heavier, and the wind brought great sheets of it sweeping across the gull colony. Soon both wind and rain were reaching into the warmth of Argen's refuge. He pushed against his mother's wing.

At dawn, he looked at a dark and angry scud in the sky. Bitter cold had settled over the island and urgent food calls passed among the gulls. The rain began again. Argen stood up and flapped his stubby wings and shook his head clumsily. Then his mother was gone into the dark sky and he was alone. The calls of the gulls matched the melancholy aspect of the streaming gullery. Argen tried hugging the ground. It was soaking wet. The disintegrating nest sprawled around him. He stood up, shivered, shook himself again. He was miserable. Then his father brought food and he gobbled it down and felt the warmth it immediately created.

The day passed in alternating moments of misery and expectation. The rain hissed down endlessly, rain that ran in runnels down the faces of the cliffs, that scoured channels in beaches, that poured down on hunched, motionless seabirds everywhere. Nestling birds at first trembled, became comatose, then died, their lives ending so suddenly that their parents kept standing over them, crops or beaks filled with food, waiting vainly for importuning beaks to reach up for the food.

On the mainland, a river rose between widespread banks, and living, dying, and dead creatures came steadily downstream. Shellfish were scoured out of sand and mud, dead robins floated in foam, flies circled in whirlpools, beetles drifted on their backs. The effluence of the flooded river stained the sea over a wide area after it had swept through a broad and spacious estuary and drove herring schools offshore toward the island.

Argen settled against the damp earth that night and pushed against his mother's side in a vain effort to get his gawky body under hers. But he was too big. He slept fitfully, hearing the rain pattering on his mother's back and feeling her moving uneasily. Many female gulls, upset by the incessant rain, deserted their nests. A small colony of terns lost their resistance to adversity and deserted the breeding ground. A handful of brooding mothers remained to shelter their chicks, surrounded by the debris of dead nestlings stretched out sacrificially in the rain.

Squalls ended the rain, but the aftermath of the storm lingered on for two days while the sea calmed and cinereous skies overhung the gullery. A pair of raccoons drifted far offshore on a tree trunk. Porpoises hissed past them. Herring gulls circled and cried out. Terns settled on an outflung branch and looked down. The raccoons looked at the birds and at the sea, but they did not comprehend. Occasionally they dipped their hands in the water and washed them.

Argen's survival of the long rain seemed to hasten his growth. Now food brought to him was regurgitated directly onto the ground, where he gobbled it up. If it did not satisfy him, he ran after his departing parent, screaming and flap- ping his ineffective wings. In these days, the shape of the world was coming to him in a flood of sensations. His food, sometimes partially digested, sometimes fresh, gradually began to assume precise forms. His father brought many shellfish. He watched for dark-shelled mussels torn loose by storms or accident. He dug into tidal sand flats for clams. He prowled the shoreline for snails and caught unwary crabs in the shallows. Sometimes the mangled bodies of these shelled creatures still pulsated with life when Argen gulped them down.

His mother caught many fish. She brought young herring, plucked from the sea on their way to spawn in shallow sea-waters. She brought smelt, herring-like fish that she caught as they waited offshore before entering mainland streams and rivers to spawn. She brought launce, small eel-like fishes which, though often buried in sand along with clams and crabs, were now traveling widely up and down the coast.

Day and night, food was transferred from sea to gullery in the beaks and stomachs of the thousands of breeding gulls, and the gullery expanded. The gulls' great numbers fostered an atmosphere of security to which Argen was sensitive. He looked out, dull-eyed and content, at the hot, dry slopes around him.

Suddenly he felt real terror. His parents were gone. A large black-and-white gull was nearby, watching him. The great black-backed gull, herself nesting among the herring gulls, was always alert for unguarded nests of any sort. Argen ran among the sheltering grasses, now inadequate to shield him completely. The blackback moved forward a step. Her beak was stained with egg yolk and blood. A sweep of pinion darkened the sun as Argen's father fell from the sky: his piercing cry sounded, and Argen was eagerly gobbling down crab meat from his beak.

With the growth of the young-gull population, the character of the gullery changed sharply. Suddenly, it seemed, there were thousands of ambulatory half-fledged birds wandering through the grasses and sandy patches of the gullery. Most of these young birds stayed roughly within their own territories, but here and there groups of them congregated and sunned on high points of ground. When their parents returned with food, they broke away from the group and ran to be fed.

This crossing of territorial lines within the gullery was perhaps confusing to some older birds. Argen was standing near his nearly disintegrated nest when he saw a young, gangling gull walking cautiously around the bottom of the knoll, picking up insects and pieces of discarded debris. He seemed self-contained and safe. The adult gulls in the vicinity were ignoring him. But quite suddenly hostility enveloped the youngster. A male gull dropped to a landing nearby and stood with his neck outstretched. The nestling fumbled on, apparently not seeing the adult, till, with a lunge, the big gull struck him to the ground. The attack generated a flurry of movement. Another gull ran forward even while the first gull was driving his heavy beak against the nestling's skull, breaking through feather and flesh till white bone was exposed. The nestling died. The two adult gulls walked away from the inert form sprawled on the grass. Argen, distressed by the violence, hid behind a rock.

During these early days, as Argen's feathers grew, a tuft of down formed at the end of each one; as he matured, these tufts began coming off. On breezy days the air around him was thick with natal down. The nestling gulls were clothed in mottled brown feathers, which made them seem unrelated to the adult birds in their sleek gray-and-white plumage.

Argen put his head down and beat his wings wildly. He knew he must fly. The instinct preceded the ability to do so. He cried out loudly, a piping scream. But countering this powerful urge was his dependence on his parents. He importuned them mercilessly for food. On occasion he even knocked them sprawling in his wild efforts to get at the food being regurgitated. But he needed them. If momentarily deprived of their presence or attentions, he became submissive and uncertain.

A keen sea wind came over the spruces on the eastern cliffs and Argen impulsively ran from his feeding area. His mother mewed softly. He plunged on, pumping his wings. For a moment he was airborne. He cried out, then crashed. The next day, he tried again, but the wind, stronger then, hurled him over backwards and he sprawled on the ground, smearing his feathers with excrement. But the rage to fly was with him now. On ensuing days he flew, with small assurance but with a clumsy power. He saw the gullery diminishing underneath. His mother flew below, her gray wings spread out, her head cocked over on one side as she looked up at him. He cried out, and then caught a glimpse of the flat expanse of the glistening western sea that separated island from mainland. His courage disappeared and he dropped awkwardly back to earth.

Argen quickly achieved independence in the air, and with this came independence from his parents. At first, he ate anything, scraps of discarded food, carrion, even eggshells. He still recognized his parents, but his importuning of them no longer brought any response. He followed his mother to the western edge of the island and watched her prowling for shellfish below the low cliffs. The security of the gullery area soon called him back.

But he was impelled to wander and to search. Early one morning he flew east for the first time and nervously began rising up the slope which led to the eastern side of the island. As he flew, he looked toward the ground under his left wing, and saw clots of dead spruces specked with roosting gulls and, far distant and beyond the island, the horizon starkly punctuated by a dark and massive rock, itself overhung with clouds of black birds. A colony of cormorants, black, long-necked diving birds, was readying itself for a morning's hunting.

Argen floated indecisively. The light glowed ahead of him because the spruces that crowned the rise shielded him from the dawn. He could now clearly hear the eastern sea, a solid sound, almost a rumble, sinister because its origins were well concealed from Argen's eyes. He climbed and felt the air growing turbulent. Then, at the tops of the spruces and coasting into the near-gale force of the sea wind, he was momentarily blinded by the savage reflection of the sun from an incalculable mass of sea. The water was serried into white-capped waves that erupted in a continuous mumble. Some waves rolled unbroken, others spumed at their crests, some toppled and exploded on offshore rocks. The blue sea swept round from wing tip to wing tip, with Argen balanced uncertainly in the center of it.

He struggled to absorb the scope of the spectacle, and it was moments before he saw the birds. Air and sea were dotted with thousands of wheeling creatures. He saw a gannet nearby suddenly turn and fall sheer into the water and disappear in a puff of white, and above the falling gannet were a thousand others. He saw bursts of kittiwakes, white against blue, and the black and white marks of speeding guillemots, razorbills, and murres. Above, poised and gargling with inquiring concern, a gannet looked down at him.

Once Argen was accustomed to the vastness of the view, his boldness increased and he coasted easily along the cliff, which suddenly dropped away immediately beneath him. He was still coping with the flood of impressions when the face of the cliff lengthened into view. It was tiered with countless thousands of nesting birds, murres, kittiwakes, gannets, razorbills, and herring gulls. They occupied every crack and crevice in the vertical side of the cliff, and their voices, magnified by the meeting between rock and sea, roared in Argen's ears. Now less confident, he followed the cliff, and the multitudes of birds unrolled at his right wing. The air around him was thick with fliers. Kittiwakes cried harshly at his head. Gannets planed past him and he swerved away from their path. Ahead, an explosion of birds from the cliffs and a sudden clamor sent him turning landward. He rose over a sea of gannets that whitened the clifftop, flew over a spruce-covered ridge, and, from this high position, could see in all directions. Before him a dark-green mass of trees; beyond that, the sea;

to his left, trees; to his right, the gullery. He allowed himself to drift diagonally across the path of the wind back to the gullery.

Each day brought experiences that helped dispel Argen's uncertainty. Events repeated themselves—morning visits to rock pools in search of pieces of shellfish left by adult gulls; midday dozing among groups of other juveniles; evening flights east of the island where adult gulls thronged to hunt small fish. The first time Argen saw the fish in the water, he dropped to seize one. As he hit the water the breath was jarred out of him. In odd moments of reaction against the way his life had changed, he mewed and sought food from nearby adults. But they ignored him. The need to search could not be diverted.

The search was as much for safety as for sustenance. Argen, a mere beginner, quickly found that he had only a minute perception of the hazards involved in searching. He was still unsure of his new wings in strong winds, and he approached the gannet cliffs with caution. Usually he settled on a rock well beyond the northern limits of both gannetry and gullery. On this day he looked out across the purple sea and the wind roared past his head. The sea sparkled and few gannets were visible; they were far distant, feeding on a herring run along the southern coast. The air was clear and crisp and the horizon as sharp as the edge of a shadow.

At first Argen looked uncomprehendingly at the speeding shape of the falcon. The falcon's feathers were folded tightly against his body, so that he was sheathed in a feathered skin. He had propelled himself at tremendous speed from the vertical cliffs to the north over the sea. He turned over in midair in a flourish of motion that indicated either disaster or supreme mastery of flight. Argen had never before seen a falcon. But he instantly recognized the menace of the shape, the short neck, long tail, broad wings. The falcon turned parallel to the shoreline, began climbing, rolled on his back, and then turned toward the cliffs and began a long, rapid fall to the sea. Argen was transfixed, for the falcon was now coming obliquely toward him. The bird disappeared below the level of the cliffs.

As Argen waited uncertainly, a sudden jagged rip of air sounded and the falcon passed within three wingbeats of the startled gull and, rolling over and over, shot straight up in the air in manic expression of his joy of flight. Argen fell backwards and collapsed, and his wings sprawled as though he had been struck. The falcon was so preoccupied with his flying that he did not see the gull. He rolled gracefully at the top of his climb and began another downward swoop that would take him past the cliffs again and toward the north. With the falcon gone and his aerial acrobatics now out of sight, Argen rose with the wind at his back and flew clumsily toward the spruces, lifted above them, and began a long glide down toward the distant gullery. The vision of the falcon's flight lingered agonizingly in his memory.

The summer matured and the island became familiar. Even the memory of the falcon faded when Argen learned to avoid the bird's hunting territory. He dropped into rocky coves that reverberated with the garglings of the gannets, and was spattered with their droppings. He probed among the shoreline flotsam, among hollow lobster claws, the half-eaten body of a long-dead ray, the remnants of a dogfish carcass, and the empty bodies of urchins. He found a dead fish in a mass of kelp and gulped it down; he ate some sand-hoppers and a small shrimp and an arm torn from a starfish.

Toward dusk, he rose from the cove and was drenched in

orange light. The sun was sinking into a purple haze of early evening, generating colors that ranged through softly delicate pinks, reds, and blues as the light passed through the sea's haze.

Argen flew to the other side of the island, still hungry and restless. He did not see the final descent of the sun, or the foreground passage of shorebirds hastening to gather food before night. Gulls pumped into the sun, a score of black ducks dotted the red water, and a heron thrashed along slowly against a red glowing background.

Argen glided over black spruces, and the sun finally sank into a deepening purple haze. The night came out of the sea itself and left a darkening slash on the horizon that suggested the mainland. The night closed in. Far off, the cry of a seabird began the hours of darkness.

CHAPTER · 3

The Shore

S LOWLY, and with growing anxiety, Argen was aware that the island, that familiar territory, was changing. At first his awareness of the change remained in the background, overlaid by the day-to-day sensations of life. Then he saw that many of the gulls were leaving the island. Their wings flashed in the dawn light as they headed for the mainland. While Argen prowled the shoreline, gulls moving west passed overhead steadily; they wheeled away from communal gatherings at dusk and disappeared west. The imminence of change affected Argen. He recognized his mother standing among some adult gulls on a rock. But when he gaped at her and mewed she flew away quickly.

The young gulls on the island gathered into flocks and awaited some stimulus to send them to the next phase of their lives. Argen was dozing in one of these flocks one day when he recognized his father flying nearby. He rose quickly and beat away after the adult bird. But his father ignored Argen's mewing cries and flew steadily to the west, where, as Argen hovered indecisively, he eventually disappeared.

As Argen cried out his anxiety other young gulls echoed his cries with high-pitched squeals that reflected their doubts. A few adult birds still brooded late eggs or chicks in the gullery, but the gulls' pattern of flight around the island was changing radically. The island was no longer a fulcrum of offshore life. Instead, it was becoming isolated and empty as the gulls shifted the center of their communal lives to the mainland. Gulls passed in high flight to the north and south. Gulls clustered far offshore on the water. But the attraction and usefulness of the island was finished.

Argen's world was the island and he knew nothing else. But another knowledge was growing in him. It was partially a migratory urge, partially an urge to search. All the young gulls felt it. This power pushed them, sometimes unwillingly, into new territories and spread them far and wide from the place of their birth. Argen soon knew that he must fly west. The open stretch of sea was terrifying but magnetic.

His anxiety reached a peak one midmorning when the sea was brightly gray-green under a sky of white clotted clouds. He flew along the western shore of the gullery, crying out repeatedly. Some young gulls rose quickly from nearby rocks and joined him. The birds pumped along and a rhythm of flight took them steadily west. One young gull mewed plaintively and wheeled back to the island.

With the flight well begun, the bare ocean disturbed Argen less and less. The strange and the unusual were forbidding, but more than any other shorebird's, his fears were transcended by curiosity. The sea rolled underneath. The island receded. The young gulls were alone with their fears.

At first the sea seemed empty, except for odd guillemots whisking along at wave height. But Argen soon saw a long, low, treeless island sprawled across the path of flight. He changed his course slightly to pass south of it. It was patched with birds dozing in the sun, waiting for the tide to begin running. They were the terns, great shore fishers who, though closely related to Argen and his kind, had long since adopted a supremely specialized way of life; their thin pointed wings, small beaks, teardrop bodies, and swift flight were refined into one endlessly repeated hunting activity: hovering, dropping, cutting into the water, seizing a fish, and fluttering upward while swallowing.

The gulls flew steadily on and the island sank quickly from sight. Ahead, the mainland loomed up in a confusing prolixity of detail. Low land curved around on either side of the gulls. Long lines of dunes stretched away to the south. The birds could hear the murmur of waves striking the shore. Green patches of marsh and swamp appeared. The tide was receding, leaving expanses of glistening mud and sand dotted with islets of reeds. Islands sprouted out of the deeper water, some treed, some bare. Argen saw cormorants drying their wings in the sun. A thin stream of terns poured under his right wing, having wakened and overtaken the gulls. A feeling of expectancy seemed to pass among the gulls and their wingbeats quickened.

The mud flats, dunes, and islands rolled past and gradually closed in on the flying birds. But always deep water stretched ahead, inviting them on. Around them, birds appeared in growing numbers. Argen heard a piercing uproar of gulls and saw low hills bulking out of the sheen of the horizon. The young gulls cried out. Then Argen saw gulls, a thick meandering mass of them, bleaching the water white and gray with their massed numbers. Food cries echoed harshly. The young gulls hastened onward, reassured by the familiarity of the gulls massed ahead of them, and now feeling their hunger.

They came to the feeding birds, dropped down, and joined

the squabbling, screaming multitude and hunted for their share of the shrimps being turned up in the receding tide. At once they became an integral part of the comity of mainland life. The island experience became shadowy and distant. That night, Argen slept on a strange sandbar while the tide, now turned again, chuckled at his feet.

On succeeding days, inshore life opened up before him in a multidimensional panorama. The island had been the focal point of his life; now the daily gathering in the estuary to feed became the center of his existence. He became accustomed to being lost among twenty to thirty thousand other gulls in the upwelling tide. On some days, Argen filled his crop and belly in the estuary and ate nowhere else.

He learned new things every day. He quickly discovered the difference between the hawk-shaped ospreys, which were light-colored, harmless fish hawks, and the rapacious falcons. His memory for such things was perfect, but in other ways it was faulty. The memory of his parents was no longer distinct. Sometimes Argen recognized his father in the middle of the estuary by the flaunt of his wings as he settled or by the shrillness in his voice. But Argen no longer felt that compelling attraction, that deep reaction rising in his gut at the sight of his parents. His memory of his mother came intermittently and, at its strongest, sent him walking hesitantly among groups of adults, but they ignored his mewing cries. He dreamed of his mother, that she was feeding him. The red on her beak was quite clear. But when he awoke abruptly, the sea around him was silent. Other young gulls hunched in sleep at his shoulders. The light was tinting the surrounding sandbar pearly gray. He cried out. Other gulls answered his cries. Anxiety swept through them. Argen took off, and was not reassured by the dawn. All day he hunted the estuary and brushed wings with a hundred gulls. Next morning his anxiety was gone.

As the days passed, Argen learned the configuration of his new territory. The estuary itself was long and deeply channeled down the center, and spotted with scores of islands. The most prominent of these were covered with pine and spruce and were shaped like gulls' wings, with gentle slopes running down to their northern edges and red cliffs slashing their flanks on the southern side. These were slowly being eaten away by occasional floods. As the estuary moved to the open sea, it shallowed, and as a result of the great quantities of sand and mud deposited by the water, became almost a delta area. To the north, black and blue lines of distant cliffs showed where a new structure of the land began, rocky and broken.

The delta area fanned out directly into the open sea and released its river water in the direction of the various offshore islands—extensions, long since separated by the work of the sea, of northern coastal cliffs. The first of these was the island of terns, worn down to nothing but a landing place. Beyond this was the offshore island of the gulls and gannets. It had once been part of a massive ridge of rock that had sprung from the mainland. The sea had long ago demolished the ridge, leaving the island detached.

Argen flew south into a flat and featureless land. Marshlands spread out before him and pools of dark water glinted in the sweeping embrace of long grasses. Streams wound mysteriously through the luxuriant growth, disappearing into the vegetation, reappearing to create a sand-bottomed pond, broadening and narrowing haphazardly in their steady movement to the sea. Argen caught glimpses of rails stalking cautiously through the undergrowth or standing motionless in reflecting pools; and, in the distance, herons beat heavily along the fringes of the marsh.

Argen let himself down over one of the marsh pools and landed lightly, then beat clear for a moment, sensing something wrong. He dropped into the water again and experimentally tasted it. It was his first experience of fresh water. It felt cleansing, refreshing. He drank deeply, then began bathing so vigorously that the pool was soon a mass of small dancing waves.

The fascination of the marsh stayed with Argen during the rest of that day as he prowled this new territory. He found that the marshlands were protected from the sea by dunelands, great sweeping sand mountains, rippled and bland, peaked and rounded, edged with grasses, stunted trees, and marked with tracks, drag marks, signs of struggles, piles of feathers. He saw the precise shadow of his own form branded on the sand. Finally, the dunes rose sharply into a massive ridge; beyond it lay the ocean beach. Argen roamed on south, over lakes set like prisms into the sand, over lagoons that studded the shoreline and let themselves into the sea through tortuous channels.

The day faded, but Argen stayed in the marshlands as the shore turned gold and green in the last suffusion of the day's light. He flew and watched and saw the evening creatures coming to life. Rails fluttered weakly from one marsh pool to another and minks ran along the fringes of the lakes where invisible fish roiled the water in sudden chases. At dusk he rested on the ocean beach, settling comfortably among a small group of juvenile gulls. He dozed while white stars rose from the black horizon.

Ocean and land opened up before him as the days passed. He saw the dark bodies of predatory fish moving slowly through the shallows, and the ocean spotted with the pulsing bodies of jellyfish. Argen passed over excited coalitions of gulls and was drawn from one flock to another. He saw foxes prowling the dunes and divined danger from their lithe bodies.

He was an uncomprehending watcher of the thickening flood of shore-hunting birds that were gradually moving south after breeding in Arctic tundra, on northern islands and shorelines. A great population of knots, gray, thin-billed shore hunters, was building up on sand flats south of the estuary, and sometimes they would perturb Argen as they hissed past him, several thousand strong, flying in compact, cohesive masses. Argen, struggling to learn his own environment, would never comprehend the appearance and disappearance of the knots, now poised on the threshold of their annual flight deep into another hemisphere.

The tidal flats around the estuary became noisy with countless other shorebirds. Long-legged, long-billed dowitchers probed in the shallows, and groups of plovers dozed, all standing on one leg and, like the knots, awaiting a flight halfway around the earth. Everywhere, hordes of sandpipers were building up. These tiny, quick-walking gray birds surrounded Argen as he stood in the shallows, thousands of them, sometimes collecting into flocks and roaring overhead so loudly that Argen flinched and ducked away from them. The shore hunters gathered, willets and yellowlegs and curlews, and their wild calls were evocative of great open distances and the thrill of the journey.

As Argen's knowledge of this territory grew, his fears diminished. He stood on a rock overlooking the estuary. His stance was bold and adult, though his plumage was still juvenile. He felt himself filling with emotion and for the first time found himself screaming with the full authority and power of an adult bird. The screams exhilarated gulls near him and sent them flying agitatedly into the air while he filled the skies with his passion and rage.

His cries became a part of the shore. Day and night, gull cries hung in the air, keen, sharp-edged, incisive. They were graduated in scale and intensity: *koy-koy-koy, kee-kee-kee, ka-ka-ka.* And all communicated with the zestful exuberance of gull life that Argen felt clearly the moment he first saw beyond the jagged hole in his egg.

The gulls' cries reflected the mood and atmosphere of the sea. On the hottest days, the calls were oppressive, flattened, and forced reluctantly through the heat. During storms, the calls rang wildly, hysterically. *Kee-kee,* and a gull came up like a ghost out of a billow. *Kawarrgh,* and a pair of wings stood upright out of the water as a gull reached deep down for a fish. *Ach-ach-ach,* gutturally, and a silent shape hovered above a sand mountain. In the background, constantly and pervasively, *koy-koy-koy-koy* and *koy-koy-koy-koy* and *koy-koy.* This was, in a few of its many forms, the language that Argen used when he began the life of a hunter at the shore.

CHAPTER 4

The Search

T HE estuary flowed around Argen and he was caught up in its complex life. The glow of pale, silent dawns washed round the estuary islets and Argen glided, very high and watchful, while clusters of sand pipers moved like wind-driven mist across the water. A heron flew across their path and they swerved away in one disciplined movement. Gulls hovered, gulls dozed on shore, gulls clustered on sandbanks. A wispy movement of birds fled along the shadow of an island and, revealed in light, the phalaropes turned abruptly toward the rising sun and disappeared.

Argen glided toward the southern shore of a large red-cliffed island in the middle of the estuary, his attention caught by hundreds of swallows sweeping low over the water, buzzing and chattering, then turning sharply back to the cliffs, where, in a twist of tiny bodies, scores of them disappeared into burrows. Argen landed on a sandbank and saw hundreds of swallows clustering against the cliffs, squabbling noisily, then suddenly dropping silently away. A swallow soared above the cliffs carrying a white feather in her beak and a score of others quickly fell in behind her in pursuit. The dark-blue sky, the swallow's dark feathers, and the speed of her flight made the feather seem disembodied and self-propelled. The feather had a significance known only to the swallows. Sometimes, out of carelessness or eagerness, the feather was dropped. It halted abruptly in mid-air and the chasing swallows hurtled onward as though unaware that the feather had gone. But after a long moment, the feather carrier darted back, plucked the feather away, and the chase continued. Argen ruffled his feathers, and the swallows landed on the sand near him and chased one another on foot in sudden rushes, then erupted into the air with churring cries.

The smell of the sea mingled with the fruitful fragrance of the island. Impulsively, Argen flew to the clifftops and settled in sunlight that now flooded the full length of the island. Behind him, a savannah sparrow darted through raspberry bushes, her beak filled with insects for a late nestful of youngsters. In stunted spruce, a sparrow squeezed out a burst of song as he faced into the blinding reflection of the sun off the water. Argen dozed and soon his back was hot under the sun.

He wakened fully to the urgings of his developing sense of time. The tide was running. It was late afternoon. He stretched one wing away from his body, then the other, scratched himself, then set off low across flat water glowing in the sinking sun. Ahead, thick white clouds clustered along the horizon. As he flew, they rose and formed three separate lines. The sun dropped into the first line, which looked so solid that the sun seemed to collide with it. White fire shot horizontally away from the sun as it dropped and touched the lower clouds with yellow and orange and left them blazing. As the sun sank, the colors deepened and rich reds glowed like coals in the wake of fire and faded fast as the sun plummeted.

Argen reached the part of the estuary where the overturning waters were thrusting up food, and joined the screaming chorus of birds strung out across the water. No bird there had eyes for the final dissolution of the day. The sun was a hemisphere on the horizon. The lines of cloud turned orange, red, purple. Then with precipitate speed the sun was gone. Only a purple sky remained. Into this, for one brilliant moment, a double ray of light shot upward. All around Argen the birds gobbled, screamed and squawked, and filled their bellies with shrimp.

The weather cooled and the sand flats steamed with a thick mist that clung momentarily before being whisked away by light winds. The swallows were more nervous. Invisible alarms sent them exploding away from the cliffs and they marked the red sky in high blossoming arches. As these bursts expanded, other swallows, slower to apprehend the danger, hurtled from holes in the cliff. In this moment of panic, the birds were deathly silent, each intent only on escaping. Then, when no danger came, their twittering cries sounded all around Argen. He flew through and beyond them on his way to feed.

Argen's imitative urge sent him following adult gulls everywhere, and he remembered their hunting grounds. He saw a group of them collected on a sandbank and joined them. The tide was ebbing and increasing the size of the sandbar. It held a long, narrow mass of water against the shore. In this were several thousand small fish, just then growing aware of their danger. Suddenly all the adult gulls rose as the fish began to run for the open sea.

The fish bunched together, compressed into a few inches

of fast-running water flowing around each end of the sand-bar. The gulls screamed triumphantly, and soon there was frenzy. Instead of dropping to the water and rising again deliberately, Argen found himself savagely smashing down to the running fish with reckless energy. Around him, gulls faced into the wind, sharply switched the plane of their wings, and used the wind to force them to the water. They rose equally quickly. Argen caught the rhythm of the hunt. He rose with a fish in his throat, swallowed it, dropped again, seized a fish, swallowed, dived. The sandbar undulated with a mass of sharply rising and falling birds who, despite their industry, screamed incessantly. Then, abruptly, the fish were drained from their prison. Argen still cried excitedly. But the instant the last fish disappeared, the adult gulls settled and were still. One by one they rose and flew out to sea. Soon only immature herring gulls remained.

The nights were now much colder. Gusts of rain swept the strand. Some days were silent with mist. Argen watched the small groups of sanderlings, lighter-colored than the sandpipers, who were moving steadily southward. They worked the fringe of the receding or advancing tide and hunted in spasmodic bursts of energy, one moment prob-ing every patch of sand that might contain food, the next moment dozing, balanced on one foot. Argen dis-covered that the ocean beach, south of the estuary, was a good place for hunting, and for hours he walked along slop-ing wet expanses of sand which bubbled around him after the retreat of each wave. He was totally preoccupied in watching the sand for signs of life, tiny flickering movements of crea-tures burying themselves for safety or momentarily stranded. He walked, oblivious to the roaring surf at his shoulder, the piled-up masses of white water, and the distant grumble of waves striking offshore sandbars. Lone sanderlings scam-

pered ahead of him and ran into the thinly streaming water
to catch their prey while sandpipers, higher on the beach,
basked in the sun.

Argen's search for food took him many times to the tidal
flats of the estuary, where he scavenged scraps of flesh overlooked when birds fought over food. He found himself impelled to drag some of his sand-encrusted prey to the edge of
the water, where he carefully washed it. He pulled at the
carcass of a young skate left behind in the tide and so old
that none of the adult gulls would touch it. He halfheartedly
chased an adult bird who had dug some food from the sand,
but was jostled aside in mid-air by a stronger, more vigorous
older bird whose determination to rob was fierce, and successful.

Argen then understood that there was food in the sand.
One day, as the tide was about to turn, he saw a bubble of air
rising from the wet sand. He dug down and exposed a clam.
Its long muscular foot drew back into the shell. Argen felt
the spasm of the shell closing as he seized the clam. Then he
dropped it, unsure what to do.

The shell lay before him, specked with clots of wet sand.
He pecked at it dubiously and so set in motion a complicated
series of reactions within his body. When he dug for the
clam, he was merely responding to an instinctive drive. But
when the creature lay clear of the sand, a new stimulus began
flooding his senses. He felt the urge to fly. But at the same
time he wanted to break through the shell and reach the
meat that he now knew lay enfolded inside. The twin urges
made him act. He grasped the clam roughly in his beak. But
its smooth surface caused it to slip out of his grasp. Then he
was half flying, grabbing the clam again, and finally taking
off clumsily into the wind.

Even then, he still had no clear comprehension of what

was to follow. Almost instantly, he was assailed by other gulls. They harried him along the foreshore with such incessant energy that he was totally occupied in trying to save the clam from their eager beaks. Finally, after flying the full length of the tidal flats, he outdistanced his pursuers, except for one grizzled bird, who neither cried out nor came too close but flew a little behind and below him. Feeling more secure, Argen rearranged his grip on the clam and, in doing so, dropped it. Instantly the older gull shot forward and caught the clam in mid-air. He flew off across the dunes while Argen screamed his frustration. But he did not follow the gull. He could not see the other bird as he flew to the wet foreshore, rose to a precise height, dropped the clam, and immediately descended to eat from its cracked and broken substance.

Argen, despite his disappointment, stood at the beginning of knowledge that was to become a part of his instinctive behavior. Now he knew how to catch shellfish. He knew he must avoid the other gulls. But he did not yet know how to reach the meat inside the shells. For this, a complicated series of events had to unfold.

At first there was no significance in the sudden frenzied clots of gulls, the screams and clashing wings, with one gull always emerging triumphant with a shellfish. The dropping of the shellfish was also meaningless until one day a young gull dropped a clam on the tidal flats close to where Argen was standing. It smashed and he pounced on it, a wingspan ahead of the other gull. He gobbled down the flesh as fast as he could. Two days later, he dug up a clam, but during his flight he lost it to another gull. He found another, but lost it. He dug up a third, rose clear of his enemies, and this time dropped it into the shallow water of the incoming tide. He flew down and settled, but there was no sign of the clam. His confusion during this period was compounded by the occasional presence of prowling crows who stalked up and down sandbars, cocking their heads up to watch the passing gulls and making sudden dashes for dropped clams that were being fought over by gulls.

Argen could learn by observation and imitation and so improve upon his instinctive action. He saw how some gulls followed closely after a dropped shellfish. They snapped it up the moment it struck the sand. He tried this but was chagrined to find another gull ahead of him. This bird, prowling the sandflats and watching the sky, had scuttled across the sand to intercept the falling shellfish.

This bitter competition for the clams at first confused Argen. He was not to know that it affected many other young gulls, who, feeling the hostility of the adults, withdrew protectively into flocks of their own age and confined themselves to scavenging. But, caught between the hostility of the adults and the lure of clam meat, Argen's need to act increased. He learned that the sand contained many other shelled creatures. Snails abounded. Scores were caught and eaten by the gulls every day. Many of the snails also hunted clams and forced themselves through the sand in an endless search for them. But Argen found that they were visible as small mounds moving beneath the sand; this was their fatal weakness. He developed a special liking for them. One day, after gorging himself on the body of a stranded cod, he saw the destruction of a snail. Sated, he stood dozing. A snail whacked down on the sand nearby. Two gulls plunged after it, clashed in mid-air, and wheeled away across the sand, fighting fiercely. Argen looked dully at the snail. Its shell was unbroken, though its interior had been severely jarred by the fall. It remained motionless. The white sun poured down, as though calling attention to the snail and inviting predators. Long after the gulls had gone, the snail began, with infinite slowness, to open its operculum, the horny protective plate sealing the entrance to its shell. This had to be swung out of the way to permit the body to emerge. As it hinged back, it slewed the snail's shell and almost tipped it over. With the operculum now folding out of the way, the viscid body began to come out. Its slow movement suggested an awareness of the danger all around it. The snail's body protruded further, and the operculum, stuck to it, pivoted outward and became the rear end of the foot on which the snail would travel. Then, from under the leading edge of the shell, the front end of the foot emerged. It crept out till it touched the sand and so was able to hoist the shell erect. This snail was the subterranean scourge of shellfish.

The light was vividly white and passing gulls were black against it. The snail moved slowly, though there was no haven anywhere in sight. Argen started as another gull dropped down, seized the snail, and carried it aloft. In the uprush, the body squeezed back into the shell, the operculum closed down tightly. In a moment the snail was falling again. This time the shell smashed. The gull's powerful beak broke into the cracked and splintered shell, smashed liver, kidney, eyes, and the mass of brown flesh disappeared down the gullet of the bird. Deep inside the broken body of the snail, the heart still beat strongly, not having yet received notice of the death of its adjacent parts.

The fall rains clothed the estuary in gray and fell among silent legions of gulls, dozing and preening away the featureless days. The young gulls were gathering into big flocks and were joined by many other juveniles arriving late from offshore islands or from the north. All of them keenly felt this change of season, and Argen, roaming a silent shore alone, cried out frustration at the red cliffs of the big island in the estuary. The swallows, sensitive to the season, had gone.

At first the fall days were bitterly cold and sleet-laden, but then they warmed again and revived the life of the estuary. This was a pause in the movement of the seasons and time stood still. Shortly before dusk, the estuary went into a deep silence. The incoming tide shone flat and wide, ridged and rippled in places and lit by the setting sun. Unaccountably some sandpipers appeared and hunched in clots along the gray shorelines.

Three great blue herons came into this silent seascape. They flew far apart but were together. Their long legs trailed at water level and their necks doubled back and their wide, flat wings pumped them rhythmically along. They settled squarely in the reflected light of the setting sun, not far from where Argen stood on the clifftops overlooking the estuary. He watched the herons standing in monumental poses of grace and patience.

After long moments, thousands of minnows asserted themselves in the shallows. The herons waded majestically forward, their heads darting down to seize the fish, holding them for a moment at the tips of their beaks, then swallowing them in swift gulps. The fish were still alive as they went down, and sometimes a heron's neck would quiver as a muscular spasm forced the struggling fish lower down.

The sun disappeared. Black clouds gathered. The herons merged into the gray-black of the water, then rose together and flew on down the strand. They were visible to Argen's eyes only as spectral shapes moving against a flat and now silent tide.

CHAPTER 5

The Magnetic Ocean

THE waves of air that rolled over the estuary became increasingly colder, and in front of each wave came migrants. Whenever the chill abated, they halted. One morning Argen flew through a mist over the estuary and found himself among a multitude of ducks. In places they concealed the water. He flew on. The ducks seemed to be everywhere. They flanked the estuary island. They stood massed in the shallows, bathing, gabbling, feeding, preening, a multicolored mass of life. Argen flew on, disturbed by the unfamiliarity of the sight.

Later that day, he heard the rumbling of air being churned by wings. He saw coastlines moving in the distance, islands disappearing, the air quivering. The weak sun turned gray as the thickest concentration of ducks flew across it. The roar of wings faded and columns of birds flew overhead, curved to join others, folded into bigger flocks, all the while maneuvering into new groupings.

As Argen slept that night on a sandbar with other herring gulls, ice crackled around him and caught at his feet. He stamped to free them. A chill wind came through the pines of the estuary island and ruffled his feathers. He wakened fully and the night evoked a dread that had no image.

His fear persisted through the ensuing days, even though he was amply equipped to face the revolutions and disasters of shore life. Everywhere the older gulls were disappearing. One morning, many of the adults who had consorted with the immature gulls were gone. Each day fewer birds fed in the turn of the tide. The tidal upturn of food eventually became so small that Argen sometimes returned to shore baffled and still hungry.

He watched the other gulls but divined nothing from their flights. He could not know that some were flying inland to become scavengers and hunters on lakes and ponds and in open forest country. Many were migrating far south, but others were drifting south, not in a true migration but in search of easier hunting. A few even went north, apparently knowing of territories less crowded with gulls.

The cries, the chilling nights, the lines of strange birds moving along the horizon at sea, daily increased Argen's restlessness. He released some of this discomfort by repeated screaming bouts, and his wild, cracked cries aroused the gulls around him. Sometimes he cried out loudly in mid-air, sometimes while prowling in the tidal shallows, sometimes even at night, sending a ripple of apprehension through the sleepy birds around him.

His unrest was heightened by the disturbing changes in the weather. Sharp gusts of wet wind swept among the dozing gulls, and the outline of the trees along the shore dissolved in thick rain. The coast foamed as storms billowed out of the east. The disturbances drove Argen into occasional frenzies of exhilaration and he patrolled back and forth across the bursting waves in pure desire to be near them.

During one violent squall, hunting became impossible. Argen left the surf lines and flew shoreward with other gulls, headed for shelter in the lee of the foreshore sandhills. Gulls hissed up over the peaked line of sand by the score and lowered themselves into the calm air behind it. Other birds—plovers, sandpipers, small flocks of ducks—were garnered by the wind into this lee.

The strength of the wind and rain was distressing to many of the smaller birds. They grew progressively more miserable as the storm roared on. Eventually, as dusk fell, no birds flew anywhere along the coastline. The few remaining sandpipers, themselves refugees from the great flocks of the earlier part of the fall, clotted together for protection. Many of them huddled shoulder to shoulder behind clumps of grasses, formed into triangular shapes, the points of the triangles pushed against the clumps of grass.

The storm brought the sea to Argen and he was filled with its limitless power. The following morning he rose into its insistent force and allowed the great ocean beach to fan out beneath him. The wind hissed in his feathers and from his high aerial view he saw elemental confusion. The white foaming line of the ocean beach looked like an extension of the land itself, so solid was the turbulence. The dunes were bathed in a smoking gloom, partly spray and vapor hurled inland from the ocean, partly sand torn from the tops of sandhills. Everywhere Argen looked, he saw vivid and unforgettable movement. He drifted north over dunes that rippled and billowed in long weaving lines. He reached the estuary, now filled with short, chopping waves which, having entered over various sandbars and shoals, were being compressed by the narrowing banks and wildly expressed their drive to expand.

But it was to the open sea that Argen looked eventually. It

disappeared into itself and it dismayed him; but it drew him. He turned back and forth uncertainly across the bleak insistence of the wind. Excitement ran through him. With it came memories of feeding times, and of his mother, and of the red mark on her beak, and of the cries of gulls well fed and secure in their summer conclaves. The image of the offshore island was vivid and he looked into the storm in an effort to see it.

The sight of the sea and the storm set off a reaction. He turned against the wind and flew into it. He left the estuary behind and moved slowly across the steady boom of surf striking shoals and beaches. He gave his *ka-ka* call and was answered by an unseen gull, but he flew on toward the open sea.

In the violent displacement of water, Argen had difficulty getting correct bearings. But soon he heard the sea breaking on the island of terns. Then the island came into view through the murk. It was partially awash and its dead emptiness was in eerie contrast to its summer life. He flew on, felt the wind tipping him back and forth; he was now flying directly and confidently.

When the gullery island slowly humped its long bulk up out of the disorder of the sea, Argen cried out repeatedly as his juvenile food reactions became a flood of memory. The familiar southern cliffs flung his calls back harshly. He was over the top of the first line of cliffs now and the gullery was spread desolately before him. The rain had washed it clean and left only speck marks of feathers in low brush and dead trees. He flew from one end of the gullery to the other and was himself silenced by the emptiness of a place he associated with food and life.

Another familiar stimulus came to him. The grumble of

surf from the eastern side of the island beckoned to him and he flew eagerly upwind, over the upward slope of the spruces, and suddenly faced the open sea. It was empty. He glided down and looked ahead and below. The vertical cliffs were marked by wash lines of rains that had cleansed the gannetry of the signs of its summer occupants. Crevice and crack, cranny and ledge, all were empty. His mewing cries were lost in the roar of waves breaking up below him. The island was dead. In time, he lost interest and returned silently to the mainland.

Argen now felt the new season in his bones. His melancholy unrest increased and was heightened by hunger. The clams and snails were scarce in the estuary flatlands. Days passed without any food being turned up in the tide. He patrolled the ocean beaches endlessly, picking up tiny scraps of food. His hunger became greater and he joined a group of older gulls, who were hostile to him.

The strand froze that night. The cold wakened Argen frequently. He rose before dawn with a score of immature gulls and found himself being led across the dunes toward the great ocean beach. As he flew, chips of ice fell from his feet, and he felt the presence of the sea long before he could hear or see it. The gulls rose buoyantly over the ridge of sand that protected the dunes from the sea, and the hissing beach lay before them.

Some instinctive, or acquired, sense had told the gulls that the storm would bring stricken creatures to the beach. As Argen pumped over the ridge, he saw a group of gulls standing motionless on either side of a prostrate bird at the edge of the surf. He knew her plight and associated it with his fears of the unknown sea.

It was a scoter, a seagoing duck that had been caught by

the freeze. Her wings were iced together behind her back, and she had exhausted herself trying to fly. Now, after struggling ashore in the night, she lay there, worn out. The gulls stood around her impassively, expectantly. They understood that she was helpless. The sea soughed.

Argen became very thin as his feathers pulled tightly against his body. The groaning call of a black-backed gull sounded. All the gulls turned toward him. The big bird came gliding slowly along the outer line of breakers, then turned inshore, pumping steadily toward the gulls on the beach. He settled deliberately near the stricken scoter and walked up to her. The duck squawked and struggled. Without pause, the blackback drove his beak against her flank. She rolled over and in went the yellow beak again. The blows loosened the grip of the ice and the duck beat her wings to escape. But already she was crippled. Her intestines were showing. Her wings came free and she thrashed frantically, but they up-ended her and sent her skittering away from the gull and crying her despair. The herring gulls took their chance and rose in a mass and fell on the stricken duck; she was concealed by their struggling bodies. So frantic was the fight that the black-backed gull could not assert himself in the melee. Gull fought gull. Birds flung free from the fight, hanging onto each other's wings; gulls shot into the air trailing feathers.

Eventually the blackback reasserted himself. He drove away the others and fed leisurely on the mauled carcass. Then he walked down to the edge of the receding surf and washed his beak in the sea. The remaining gulls, their frenzy to eat strangely gone, bickered listlessly over the remains of the duck.

Argen was experiencing a fact of winter which could kill

him. Competition for food directed the lives of the gulls, so that they were pitted less against the environment than against each other. The most aggressive gulls fed. The least aggressive went hungry. In the ensuing days Argen saw many young gulls dying. As his hunger grew, he saw them at points along the estuary, in the dunes and on beaches, hunched in sleep at midday, crouched down, eyes dulled. Most of them died at night. By morning the bodies would have been eaten by foxes or black-backed gulls. Long before the real winter began, many of the youngsters from that breeding season were dead.

Argen survived, flung into spasmodic anger by his hunger and revealing, despite his immaturity, determination, and spirit to survive. He was constantly urged toward the sea. He flew beyond the line of breakers countless times and faced swollen humps of gray and white water and then turned back to land. On land were hunger and despair. At sea was the unknown. Both repelled him. He cried out. In his cries was the touch of primeval terror that had haunted his kind through millennia and had spurred them to success at the seashore.

The sound of the surf became louder and filled Argen's ears at night, so that he became vividly aware of dark seas rising and falling. He crouched, frightened by his dreams. The steady magnetic pull of the sea was penetrating the center of his existence.

One morning, unexpectedly, the call to the sea came. He had flown beyond the breakers and had drifted diagonally. The waves were low and white-edged and their troughs hid scattered flocks of old squaws, the most numerous sea ducks, and odd groups of eiders. The ducks rose and fell easily, then left the sea empty as they dived for fish and shellfish on the dark bottom. Argen flew on directionlessly and heard an urgent food cry. A low-flying group of herring gulls, two adults and a score of immature birds, were beating out to sea. The food cry was repeated by the young birds. Argen was hungry. The cries drew him, but the birds were flying out to sea. This confused him. Then the memory of the empty island and the dark horizon faded as the food cries persisted, and suddenly he turned and flew powerfully after them.

As the sound of the surf diminished, Argen was momentarily alone in an empty sea; the other gulls were lost in hazy spume ahead. Then a seal reared its black head from a wave and strove to peer out to sea. He submerged, and Argen flew over him. The seal's black shape sped underwater almost as fast as Argen was flying against the wind. The seal reared up again and sank. Ahead, Argen saw ducks bobbing. He overtook the other gulls, and moments later the seal rose precisely beneath a duck and pulled it down so quickly that no other duck was aware of the attack.

The gulls were now a straggling line spread across the width of the waves. Now that he had company, Argen felt safe. The chill wind, the buffeting air bouncing up from peaking waves, the desolate sough of wind, all combined to excite him. The gulls flew on, beyond the offshore island, somberly still as the sea grappled at its banks, into a vaporous distance ahead which opened and closed as sea and air, mutually disturbed, interacted to produce mist and spray. The sea was yielding easily to the determined flight of the gulls. Soon they were no longer flying blindly but faced a slackening wind coming out of an opening horizon. Other gulls flew on either side of them. Argen sensed something in the sea ahead. He called a warning, but the other gulls, absorbed, ignored him.

The gulls were now far beyond the influence of the land and were reaching into the oceanic world, a territory where seabirds feared the land as much as landbirds feared the sea. The sky lit up ahead. Puffins moved rapidly on both flanks of the gulls and disappeared into effulgent haze. Argen had never flown so far but he was not tired. Instead, he felt impelled to cry out. He glided for a moment, then screamed *koy-koy-koy-koy*, and felt a sudden release of tension.

The adult herring gulls were now forging ahead in anticipation of what lay ahead. Argen felt an urge to drop down and begin feeding, but the other birds did not pause. He began to tense in readiness for another scream, but was stopped by the sight of a large gull, almost pure white and graceful as it soared up out of a wave and rose steadily into the wind. The glaucous gull, an arctic bird that came south when feeding in the north became uncertain, cried *aaaaargh*. The guttural sound frightened Argen and he dropped to the rear of the flying herring gulls.

The eastern sky lightened and now Argen saw oceanic birds on all sides of him. A tight flock of dovekies shot past, silent and intent, their wings buzzing their chunky, thrush-sized bodies forward. As the tiny auks sped past Argen, he heard a great multitude ahead and he immediately had an impression of the gullery island, warm and peaceful under the summer sun. But the sound portended no island. Thousands of whitish forms appeared in the icy haze of the eastern horizon. The herring gulls now flew with power and authority. The sound increased and rose above the sough of the wind and the hissing break of waves. It was the sibilant, nasal buzzing and droning of scores of thousands of kittiwakes. The small gray-and-white gulls were massed along a broad track of the ocean, as though parasites on the body of the water itself. Colliding ocean currents were lifting masses of planktonic life—eggs, larvae, and young of many sea creatures—and pursuing this were hordes of hungry herring. The kittiwakes were eating plankton and small fish and were present in such great numbers that Argen could see only a small part of them. They wound on across the sea out of his sight.

The herring gulls flew on steadily till, deflected by the number of kittiwakes rising, they turned and flanked them. At last the adult herring gulls turned down toward the water and the flock spread and settled. Suddenly fish appeared all around them. Argen squawked, jabbed a fish, and swallowed it. The gulls became absorbed, but as Argen struggled to swallow a fat herring a kittiwake was beside him almost immediately, jabbing at pieces of the herring that Argen had torn loose. A score of kittiwakes clustered around him and so confused him that he regurgitated the fish. As he tried to rip pieces from it, the kittiwakes jostled him; he flew away and saw them diving for the sinking scraps.

The gulls had settled at the flank of the densely clustering kittiwakes, but now, with fish rising all around them, they were overwhelmed. Like snow, kittiwakes settled around Argen again. Already dazed and confused by the screaming, the density of the beating wings, the thrusting of small beaks, the encircling battery of beady, eager eyes, he finally rose heavily and slashed his way to freedom. As he climbed, he veered and settled at a distance from the multitude. There he fed on odd stragglers that had drifted away from the main body of the hunted fish.

Gradually he became accustomed to the uproar of the kittiwakes, and when his appetite was satisfied, he joined two adult gulls and flew east. The three birds flew and glided leisurely for half an hour, but there was no break in the kittiwake masses. When the gulls turned back, the kittiwakes were rising and flying toward them. They were almost silent now, and as they whisked past Argen, he saw the surface of the water spattered with thousands of tiny droppings. There was no sign of life in the sea. The great upsurge had ended, the plankton had folded back into the sea and with it the herring. Ahead, herring gulls were also rising, but they were turning west, toward the land, and so the two types of gulls passed each other on unalterable courses.

Argen sensed that the feeding time was over. The mainland exerted a strong pull and he had no will to resist it. He pumped along after the older gulls. Behind him, the last of the kittiwakes disappeared into a freezing east wind.

During the rest of that winter, Argen gradually became familiar with the rhythms of the offshore hunt. He listened for food cries relayed across the open sea and became sensitive to combinations of temperature and humidity which suggested that fish might be at the surface. While the winter kept killing the young gulls, Argen thrived and grew strong. While his comrades lost voice and spirit and disappeared, he became more confident and aggressive. His voice acquired that masterful quality which proclaimed growing maturity. In this way, he passed through the winter and into the spring and so to the second summer of his life.

CHAPTER 6

Spring

THE dunes, bleached by winter, turned green. The dark sea, chilled by the Arctic, grew warm. White skies ripened and became blue. Oceanic birds drifted north in expectation of the thawing of their near-Arctic breeding grounds. Migrants moved north along the coastline and the cries of geese at midnight raised the hackles of foxes hunting in the dunes.

Petrels came cautiously out of the open sea one misty night and reoccupied their burrows on the offshore island. Soon, the red cliffs of the estuary island would echo to the calls of gulls one evening and would be softly spiked with twittering swallow cries at dawn. Argen floated across water glittering with trembling lights and faced a wind that brought warmth instead of snow.

He remained a victim of the present, often driven by the immediacy of events into some new action. He hovered at the fringe of judgment. He came out of the past with memories, often incisively clear, which gave his personality a precise quality that enabled him to make simple, intuitive estimations. He could interrelate incidents and reach conclusions; he was a learning creature. He knew the difference between a sportive falcon, usually a young one who flew for pleasure, and an adult falcon whose only objective was food. He had learned to recognize certain combinations of times, temperatures, and air pressures which meant that small fish would be rising to feed at the surface. Thus he knew when to set off in search of them, ranging widely across the inshore sea, in daylight or in darkness.

In the recesses of his simple brain lurked a suggestion of higher life. But most of the time, as his skin prickled with the excitement of spring, he reacted automatically to the stimuli of the moment. The need to preen came to him. Preening expressed his confidence and, in his idle moments, he practiced it almost constantly. It was a ritual that was both practical and sensual. As always, he turned first to his back feathers and gently teased them with his beak so that all the tiny barbules that hooked the feather spines were thoroughly disturbed. The barbules would then hook into the adjacent barbs and so ensure the sleekness of the feathered sheath. His preening restored his wing feathers, which needed constant attention if they were to remain effective. If unpreened, barbules became unhooked, the feathers became ragged and were liable to break. The only parts of his body that Argen could not reach were the top of his head and the back of his neck. He took care of these areas just as effectively by tensing skin muscles which raised the feathers. He would then lift a leg and vigorously kick the feathers while rotating his head to disturb every part. At the end of his preening, he would shake himself. A shower of fine debris would drift away in testimony to the thoroughness of his work.

The gusty impatient winds of spring blew him, skew-winged, across the estuary. He was developing individual traits, distinct among the thousands of gulls around him. As the certainty of his power expanded, the tension of his muscles decreased and he developed the habit of flying with slow, relaxed deliberation, dangling his legs as though about to land.

As he flew, he witnessed the repopulation of the estuary. Hastened by spring rains, the snow melted in the hills, and the water ran over leaves and bare soil, through mud and gravel, and became enriched with salts, the products of the previous growing season in the forest. The water flushed into streams and rivers and poured through the estuary to the sea.

Argen flew in a wide curve across the estuary as clots of bubbles, patches of scum, and floating debris moved with the tide and an enormous reaction occurred, unseen, underwater. Billions of tiny plants, diatoms, which had been dormant during the winter, were stirring and were being carried toward the surface. Though invisible, they were Argen's link to the source of all life, the sun. The sun warmed the backs of his wings and poured energy into the diatoms. They synthesized its light, and the salts of the land, and, at times, doubled their numbers every hour.

As the diatoms multiplied, they became visible, and as Argen passed across a bay, the sun sinking at his right wing, he saw the water discolored in a long streak where currents had swept together a visible concentration of the tiny plants. He landed among them. Beneath, the darting forms of herring plucked away at the diatoms. As Argen peered down for a sight of the herring, he could not know that the diatoms were being engulfed by myriads of copepods, tiny animals with wriggling tails. He swam quickly forward to a mass of almost transparent shrimp which were eating both copepods and diatoms and which themselves were being eaten by the herring. Argen ducked his head down and scooped up beakfuls of shrimp.

As he harvested at the heart of oceanic life, he was well removed from an important part of the reaction to spring that was taking place in the sea. Far offshore, populations of adult salmon were building up in readiness for their run up the estuary and the river system where they would spawn. Legions of squid moved along the surface toward the shore. In submarine gullies, many relatives of the herring gathered for their runs toward fresh-water rivers and streams. They included smelt, which would swarm upstream in uncountable millions. There were shad, much larger and heavier fish, which were almost as numerous as the smelt and which would spawn in streams so shallow that their backs would glisten in the open air as they flicked themselves over slippery rocks.

The migrant fish gathered, and so did the cod and haddock, dark-scaled fish, some longer than Argen's outstretched wings, which prowled the ocean bottom and ate various fish and shellfish, crabs and young lobsters. They moved inshore in pursuit of smaller fish and passed over adult lobsters which, feeling the slight warming of the waters, were rousing from winter somnolence. Above the cod and lobsters passed many eels, heading for the rivers to reproduce. The water became green with the life growing in it, then lightly striated as stronger sun shone through it.

The change of season was dynamic. Argen screamed at his comrade gulls who were collecting in the estuary and they answered him with whistles and screams. King crabs moved their primitive hemispheric bodies into shallower water and more highly developed crabs with claws swam to the shoreline seeking new territory to accommodate an increase in their numbers.

The young Argen grew daily stronger and more confident. Whether hunting alone or flying offshore almost beyond the sight of land, he was exploring his environment to its limits and to the extent of his own resources. But though he was constantly expanding his range and sophistication, he was still a juvenile. This was plainly revealed by his brown plumage, which contrasted with the sleek whiteness of the adults. If he contested an adult gull, he was dealt with peremptorily; the adults always assumed that their authority was superior.

But now he shared with other young gulls an expectation of great events. The adult herring gulls were filled with a rising excitement. Argen watched, uncomprehending, as adults rose suddenly together from the estuary in a blooming flight which spread from bank to bank. He joined a small group of juvenile gulls standing on a rock. *Ka*, he cried, but his cry was lost among the piercing calls of the screaming adults. He became silent, a witness.

Flying from inland, from north and south, the adult gulls gathered in clustering lines on banks, dunes, rocks, and foreshore. They hastened up and down the coast, and fought each other and swept over Argen's head and drew other adults up to them with their cries and disappeared out to sea.

Argen stood apart, puzzled. White clouds changed patterns in a bright, windswept sky. A sudden uproar exploded a group of gulls into the air and Argen felt himself drawn up with them. As he beat upward, he saw a thickening of gulls over the eastern end of the estuary, and these birds began drifting out to sea. But Argen's excitement died. He dropped down to the island and watched the gulls dwindle to the east.

This was a time of plenty. Estuary and delta, stream and

pond, swamp and ocean, were so well stocked with herring, smelt, squid, shrimp, and minnow that Argen caught his fill of food in a small fraction of his waking hours. One day in early spring he had fed with his father in the estuary and had recognized him but had felt nothing. His father had not recognized him. There was no use for any bond between the two birds now and so no provision was made for it.

The young gulls were held in the loose comradeship of their juvenility, but they were all uncomfortable and restless. Some young gulls, nervous and uncertain, went on solitary migrations. Others followed the adult gulls to the offshore island and so became part of the larger life experience there.

Argen watched the gulls flying offshore and associated them with the island. His memories of the island were good. But he hesitated to leave the greater familiarity of the estuary. One day he heard the excited *kee-agh, kee-agh, kee-agh* of an offshore-flying gull and he succumbed to the pull of the island. He flew rapidly down the estuary and had no eyes for the passing islands, the spreading mud flats, the flat green patches of sunken eelgrass.

The sea was benign, bristling with sparkling points of light from a sun that had not yet reached its zenith. The terns somnolently blanketed their island. Far off, the gullery island appeared and Argen quickened his wings in fugitive memory of his mother. The white specks of floating birds against dark cliffs quickly enlarged into the endless detail of the gullery.

He was now over the western cliffs. He called to the thousands of gulls spread out beneath him. He received no answer and he turned confidently against the wind. He looked down for a place to land and quickly saw the most desirable area, a prominent knoll rising in the center of the gullery. The gull pairs were most thickly clustered around and on it. He turned toward the knoll and landed. Immediately he was surrounded by gulls with lengthened necks who menaced him by the very tenseness of their bodies. Finally, when he remained on the knoll, he was challenged by an adult male who, after a series of long cries, charged and knocked him sprawling. The attack made him submissive; but he was also outraged at its unexpectedness. Up to then his experience had clearly told him that it was safe to consort with adults. He was knocked down again, struggled finally into the air, and flew beyond the gullery. He looked suspiciously now at the motionless gulls standing on the sweeping green of the knoll, in the dead white spruces, on rocks, and in bushes. The gulls seemed peaceful and familiar. Argen cried out his solitary doubts. He did not understand the strict territorial rules. The attacks warned him that he did not know the gullery.

As he glided over the eastern cliffs, he saw the gannets thickly massed and turned away from them, toward the gullery. But gulls flying all around him, some crying out, some silent, gulls watching him from the ground and from dead spruces, made him conscious of hostility and of the unknown. Nevertheless, he dropped down, drawn by an overmastering desire to be with the gulls. He was about to land when the rigidity of a gull's neck warned him that his approach was resented. He cried out his apprehension with a half-submissive *uh-uh-uh* and flew on.

A clear patch of ground with a white stone on it caught his eye and he settled on the stone. He was surrounded by tall necks and intent eyes. Self-consciously, he preened his wing feathers. While doing so, he saw a gull approaching. He was a large powerful bird and his movements were menacing as he trod carefully among the stones and sticks.

Argen turned to face him and felt his skin prickling and the muscles tensing in his neck and chest. The big bird paused nearby. His neck was raised and his head was pointed down. The intensity of his stance was menacing. Then the shoulders of his wings gradually moved away from his body. Argen, caught in uncertainty by this behavior, responded by turning sharply toward the strange gull, anticipating an attack. But the other gull lowered his head and with a series of savage jerks ripped chunks of grass loose from the gound. In doing so, he hauled up roots, clods of earth, and small stones. Argen felt his neck stretching up and his wings moving away from his body as he anticipated fighting. The big gull responded by slowly circling him, ripping and digging with mad energy that gradually constricted Argen's senses. *Rip-rip-rip*, and the grass flew. *Rip-rip-rip*, and a clod struck him on the head. *Rip-rip-rip*, and finally Argen was triggered into action and flew frantically and rose above the gullery with an apprehensive downward glance to make sure the big gull was not following him. Now he felt relief suffusing him. The sea sparkled all around him and he was free.

But his sense of freedom did not last long. His instinct to be with the other gulls was persistent and undeniable. In midafternoon he came away from a roost on some offshore rocks and tried again to land in the gullery. He was chivvied, menaced, bitten, and driven off. He rose into a spruce but was driven out of that. Accidentally, he landed where there were no gulls within a dozen wingbeats, no nearby nest. He was ignored as he stretched up his neck in stiff expectation of another attack. It did not come. In this way, he learned that he could occupy the peripheral areas of the gullery, or thinly settled areas within it, and there he found other birds like himself—widowed birds, juvenile birds, sick birds, and old birds—and he joined them and looked at the hard, resistant face of the gullery all around him.

Spring

The gullery island, which Argen clearly recalled from his nestling days, was quite a different place to a young gull in his second summer of life. He flew east, over the spruces, into a raging red sky which washed him crimson, and saw the tall forms of the gannets silhouetted against the color. At first, he felt no hostility from them. But some of the large birds soon flew closely parallel to him, gargling softly. He dropped down to fly against the vertical cliffs. Immediately kittiwakes boiled out from the crevices and cried out. Some murres flew silently overhead, making no hostile gestures, but their close flight seemed significant and he veered away.

Eventually he tired of the antagonism and flew out to sea and did not return till evening. The long length of the island was darkening against the setting sun. The air was moving with hunting and fishing birds. Gannets dropped vertically and raised tall columns of water. He landed on the water among a thousand murres and razorbills, and ahead he could see the sharply ducking forms of puffins. At dusk he rose and returned to the gullery.

During this second summer of his life, Argen remained at the gullery. He watched while the gulls mated, incubated, fed each other. He became a prowler, a scavenger at the periphery of the gull metropolis, and lived on overlooked scraps of regurgitated clam, herring, smelt, and shrimp.

He consorted with some other juvenile gulls, who, being inexperienced and insecure, thronged together. In their gatherings they were a microcosm of the gullery itself; they clustered along the island foreshore and sunbathed on offshore rocks and squabbled with insistent high-pitched squeals of hunger, frustration, and assertion. Their camaraderie was uneasy and frequently erupted into violence as the young birds tested their authority. During this period, Argen's authority among the other juveniles increased steadily. He landed in the middle of a mob of squabbling juveniles and they deferred to him, mindful of beatings he had given many of them. The power of his rage and personality dominated them.

In establishing ascendancy, Argen learned he could dominate some older gulls, even the dreaded black-backed gulls whose depredations at the gullery were still in his memory. He was feeding alone one day on the shapeless wreckage of a haddock which had become stranded in a crevice among some shoreline rocks. Its body had already been ripped and mauled by other marine predators. Argen became conscious, as he fed, that a black-backed gull was watching him from a nearby rock. Eventually the blackback stepped into the water and swam slowly toward him.

For a moment Argen was intimidated and stepped away as the big black-and-white bird rose abruptly out of the shallows. But then, as the other gull began feeding, rage filled Argen. He uttered a high-pitched whistle, or scream, stretched out his neck, and circled the blackback. At the same time, he reinforced his desire to attack. The intensity of his thin cries and the menacing position of his shoulders could not be ignored by the blackback. He looked uncertain, then stepped quickly away as Argen, sensing a weakening of purpose, rushed forward to the haddock. Then, feeding again, he saw the blackback swim to his rock and mount it, and the incident was ended without fighting.

The gullery island became swathed in soft summer winds which clung lovingly to the grasses and caressed the feathers of thirty thousand newly hatched gulls. The gullery was fecund because of the seasonal bounty of food. But now it was seriously overcrowded. The resources of sea and shore were not equal to feeding the colony. Argen's dominance over the other gulls assured him of fair hunting. But in the gullery itself there was rising tension.

Gull fought gull in the steaming heat of midday and ripples of conflict sped among the spruces. Argen and his juvenile fellows were joined by hundreds of young gulls floating in from the mainland as though in response to a hidden signal from the gullery and hunger spurred them to act. They became prowlers at first, then plunderers.

The sun burned harshly through an amorphous sea haze. Argen and his comrades stood near a group of adult gulls. A female gull rose from her nest and flew away; her mate moved to guard the nest. With a quick rush, Argen ran to the nest, seized an egg, and flew off. In the riotous confusion that followed, another juvenile seized a nestling and fled, the young bird half swallowed. Gulls collected in fierce exchanges of cries while, far distant, Argen ate the egg and cleaned his beak on a rock with two glancing swipes against its rough surface.

Soon the need to plunder became paramount and kept the juveniles from attempting any other hunting. Now Argen felt himself spurred to feed at the gullery exclusively. To do this successfully, he needed to breach the defenses of the nesting birds regularly and quickly. He learned how. Because all the nests were so closely guarded, any attack had to be a surprise. When flying over the gullery, Argen saw many unbrooded eggs of gulls who had not yet begun incubating. But when he turned down to investigate, he was immediately intercepted by adults and sometimes beaten.

One day, however, flying very low, he managed to pillage two nests. Thereafter, he would fly slowly, almost at ground level, and pounce on nests so quickly that he could scoop up an egg or a chick and be away before the parents could reach him. He became a familiar sight, half gliding, half flying, silent against the yellowing grasses of summer. He could either pierce the egg and carry it clipped in his beak, or stretch his mandibles wide and carry the egg intact. He even found he could swallow the egg entirely and regurgitate it later, still intact. In twenty days he destroyed nearly one hundred eggs.

During the rest of the summer, he was chased constantly by angry gulls while the breath whistled into his lungs, cramped by the bulk of egg or flesh in his throat. Other juveniles, sensing his success, followed his marauding flights and exploited the confusion he caused. Toward the end of the season, he used a new method of robbing. Once when he ventured near a nest an adult gull menaced him. Argen instantly became submissive. The adult gull relaxed. Still in his submissive stance, Argen stepped forward. The adult ignored him. Argen walked past him and had half swallowed the nestling before the guardian gull reacted with a scream and an attack.

The hot summer days droned monotonously with the sound of flies and the cries of sparrows and the buzzing voices of distant kittiwakes. The crop of gulls' eggs and nestlings suffered large losses. As a result of the depredations of the young scavenging gulls, who now numbered more than five thousand, fewer than one nest in five produced fledglings. One hundred thousand eggs were laid at the gullery but only about twenty thousand fledglings flew. Argen and his fellow scavengers kept the gullery an arena of nervous alarms.

He stood in a dead spruce at dawn, the brilliant sun behind him, and felt strange powers within him.

CHAPTER 7

The Gale

ONE morning Argen felt his skin prickling at the approach of a storm. He flew over the gullery and voiced his disturbance with shrill cries. His juvenile comrades rose beneath him as he flew and, spontaneously, he turned along the western shore. The other young gulls fell in loosely behind him. The sea was placid but the falling sun had an eerie yellowish quality. The yellow blazed, then dissolved into somberly glowing grays. The gulls hung poised in the light. *Kaa-waraagh*, they called inquiringly at the sun. Argen turned down toward an offshore rock and the young gulls settled densely around him. Their serried ranks were dark fantasms lit yellow and then orange as the birds warily watched the interplay of sunlight and cloud shadow. In the middle of a burst of bright sun, rain fell. An uneasy wind fled across the island and puffed the birds' feathers. The silent sea came to life. Gray waves appeared and black clouds slid over them. As the wind swelled, the juveniles scattered, some returning to the island, others heading for the mainland. Argen flew alone to where some cormorants were nesting and scavenged till it was night.

The moon appeared briefly, turned on and off by the now fast-moving clouds. Eventually its light was doused completely. Only the swelling roar of the sea told of the growth of the storm. At midnight the rain fell solidly. It hit shorelines scarcely prepared for the massiveness of its arrival. This was not the season for tempestuous rain or wind. The water hissed into the spruces, and on impact splashed into a haze across the gullery. Argen, standing on a rock island, was almost breathless from the density of the spray surrounding him. Confused birds blundered about in the darkness.

Growling sounds were whipped away by the wind as puffins, clawing their way to the surface against inrushing floods of water, called their alarm into the darkness. On bare rocks, cormorants faced into the wind and crouched down close to the bare and streaming earth. Runnels of water ran between their legs and carried away the nesting debris; odd eggs rolled in the water and fell over the cliffs into the sea.

The mainland swallows, their deep burrows in the earth occupied by late, unfledged nestlings and by the adults, were safe and dry. They slept. But few other creatures did. Argen rocked back and forth as gusts of wind sped among the birds in the gullery. When the sky lightened slightly, he took to the air with relief and his wings grappled with the force of the wind as he was flung about. Wild cries rose from the gullery. A spirit of urgency, excitement almost, reached Argen and he allowed himself to be hurled away to the west in a great parabola which took him over the lee shore of the island, where the hiss of the surf came to him with a ventriloquistic voice. He drifted in the lee to the northern end of the island and then heard the real sound of the storm. It was sound set upon sound and surmounted by the wail of the wind ripping the tops off waves. He pushed uneasily past the northern cliffs into the full force of the wind and saw the white chaos of waves belting against the shore. A gannet was dwarfed in the spume, trying to claw up onto a rock. He had been caught by a gust of wind and had been dashed against a rock. Now, one wing broken, he had no choice but to clamber among the rocks or take his chances in the surf.

Argen passed on, facing directly into the wind and drifting crosswind to move along the shore. He saw young and old kittiwakes clustered along their nesting ledges apprehensively watching the rising sea. A puffin bolted out of some rocks, took to the air, and remained motionless, wings invisible, unable to make headway against the wind. The puffin teetered, let himself down, dropped his feet, got half a grip on a rock, lost it, was swept back and tumbled among the rocks, and so passed from Argen's sight.

All the oceanic birds were troubled by the storm. It was perhaps the gravest danger of their lives. The murres, razorbills, puffins, guillemots, all needed space to maneuver. In calm weather their landfalls were clumsy enough, but in storms all landings were hazardous, as these birds paid the penalty for being so supremely specialized at swimming instead of flying. Argen saw odd dark bodies in the whiteness of the surf. Some murres and razorbills had miscalculated the force of the storm at dawn and had lost their lives against the rocks which were meant to be their refuge. Murres peered out inquiringly at Argen from slits in the rock and he saw a pair of razorbills huddled together on a ledge. He passed on, balancing himself trickily against the thrust of the wind.

The gannets, the most powerful fliers at the shore, passed majestically overhead to offshore hunting territories and disappeared into the murk. Despite the tumultuous conditions, they had discovered a school of herring and were lancing into the waves by the thousand, unencumbered by the storm.

Argen allowed himself to be carried around the southern foreshore of the island. With the wind behind him, he was seized in its grip; he tipped forward, recovered his balance, and then swept on in a blurring rush of speed. The island of terns appeared out of the murk, then disappeared instantly, leaving him with an impression of huddled, miserable birds.

Other gulls were airborne, all heading for the mainland. Argen felt drawn toward the ocean beach and he turned diagonally and headed south rather than into the estuary. Almost immediately, he heard the rumble of surf. It was a wild, forbidding, exciting sound. He pumped forward eagerly. The sea whitened over some of the shoals where waves, deflected, twisted and crashed into each other. Screams sounded and Argen was suddenly among gulls rising and falling along the surf.

The storm was causing many victims to become stranded. Some were crabs which, floating in seaweed after having been torn away from more sheltered places, now found themselves about to be cast up on the most exposed part of the coastline. Some of the victims were small fry which normally took to shallow water to escape from predatory mackerel and pollock but which, in the turmoil of the storm, became confused and, in the grip of the waves, were carried into the foaming shallows. The gulls dived in and out of the surf with the assurance of creatures who were masters of the storm. When Argen first dropped into the water, he was frightened by the toppling height of the waves around him. He rose without seizing a fish. But his confidence grew, then vaulted into recklessness as his crop filled.

A wave caught him and carried him back in its foaming crest. He was buried under a boiling mass of water but, a moment later, he shrugged clear and hovered, at wavetop, ready to seize another victim of the storm. The wind rose in force. Soon it was stronger than anything in Argen's experience. One by one, the gulls were deserting the beach. They disappeared over the sandy hill that shielded the hinterland marshes and dunes from the ocean. Finally Argen was tired and replete. He turned and allowed himself to be carried at high speed over the sand barrier and deep into the marshlands. He dropped down to the comparative calm of the flats and landed among a thousand other herring gulls.

Argen experienced only a tiny part of the storm. As he dozed, the storm ground against the shore with increasing force, its power not even partially dissipated by the impact with rock and sand. It rebounded back into the sea. As each wave broke inshore, it had to overcome a contrary force coming away from the shore, a powerful underwater current, a broad, flat jet of water escaping from the pressure of the storm against the shore. In some places, this current scoured the bottom and ripped weeds loose and carried them out to sea. There they floated and so were brought back inshore to be cast up on the strand by the waves.

Inshore, the underwater region was a streaming turmoil of conflicting currents. Schools of fish were split up as opposing currents bore them away. The water reverberated with the rumble of the waves hitting and the grinding noise of boulders and stones being moved by deep storm currents. Some boulders were carried among colonies of shellfish and many were crushed even while they were spinning fresh threads of anchoring substance to fasten themselves more firmly to stones and rocks.

The tiny creatures sheltering in the seaweed—crabs, shellfish, small fish, and others—faced dubious futures when the storm ripped the seaweed loose. Once they were cast on the shore, they would wait helplessly until the shorebirds found them or the sea carried them back to safety.

The storm did not diminish that day and the night brought new kinds of victims to the shore. These were stricken oceanic birds, unseen except by knowledgeable foxes patrolling the beaches and by odd raccoons who chanced on them inland. They came from the inshore area and from the deep ocean. Petrels came out of their burrows on the offshore island that night and were caught in the wind. Many of them, after long struggles, were carried to the mainland. Even as Argen slept, petrels were flying helplessly overhead, some to come down in the dunes, others to find refuge in grasses and reeds and in ponds, all of them exhausted.

Many other birds came out of the deep ocean that night. They included puffins and juvenile razor-billed auks, which, at the beginning of the storm, had occupied stations far offshore. They came inshore gradually, alternately settling on the water and flying in vain efforts to beat away offshore. In each flight, they skittered along at wavetop height, driving diagonally into the wind but being forced relentlessly toward the invisible shore.

Shortly before dawn, the young auks began arriving at the coast. It was a graceless arrival. Some hit trees, struck the sides of dunes, fell into marsh streams. Some burrowed so deeply among reeds that they drowned. The puffins were less distressed, and small and watchful groups of them collected along the whitened beaches, anxiously looking out to sea for the first slackening of the wind which would enable them to get offshore again.

Dawn revealed the night's destruction. The herring gulls were aloft and excitedly flying long before there was any sign of light. From a dunehill, Argen looked down on odd victims spotting the beach. Withdrawing waves cocked up the wings of drowned seabirds. He walked past six dead immature herring gulls, drowned in some enveloping disaster. He pulled at the sodden body of a dead puffin, but abandoned it when he discovered a number of small dead crabs being swept up the surfline. By midday he had scavenged so much food that his crop became overfilled and refused to accept any more food. He vomited the excess onto the sand and stood on the bare, roaring beach, his neck distended and his feathers fluffed out.

All during that day, the wind diminished but the waves stayed high. In this aftermath, the residual effects of the storm began. The big island in the estuary—the sanctuary of the swallows, who were now fleeting through gusty cinereous skies—lay wet and silent. The torrential rains had soaked into the soil at the top of the cliffs. The soaking had gone so far down that portions of the cliffs were rifting deep in the interior. Some of the swallows, running to the depths of their cliff barrows, found falls of earth obstructing them.

The blustery day turned to evening. The swallows disappeared into the colony in the cliff face. The first fall of earth occurred silently. A mass of earth dropped to the beach, taking with it more than five hundred swallows, adults, nestlings, and fledglings. One bird, sleeping near the entrance of his burrow, struggled clear and fled away from the falling earth. After the fall, another bird rose from the red mass of fallen earth and arced out over the estuary with a chuckling churr. Swallows elsewhere along the cliffs stirred and twittered as they felt the impact of the fall. Here and there, birds bolted from the face of the cliff, perhaps in response to memories of previous falls.

Meanwhile, on the offshore island, still darkly beset by

waves, young and old kittiwakes clustered along the ledges of the eastern cliffs. The lowest ledges were close to the tops of the waves, and after each burst of energy against the rocks, spume flashed up and struck the cliffs. The kittiwakes crouched against rock that constantly streamed with water. When an extremely large wave came humping out of the gloom, some of the kittiwakes divined danger and broke away with buzzing cries of warning. The wave came on, not breaking, but menacingly silent and fast. It was so huge it did not topple and break but rose up the cliff face in a black mass. It almost reached the bottom ledge of kittiwakes, and the young birds, terrified by this unexpected approach of the water, broke away in scores. Many of them could not fly and they struck the water and fell with it. The wave dropped back into itself with a rush and out of it projected the upthrust wings of the kittiwake youngsters.

The waves diminished only slightly during the night, and the sleeping gulls on the mainland stirred uneasily when, periodically, huge waves struck the shore in explosions that shook the ground. Rocks broke, debris was hurled high up the shore, shorebirds fled silently along smoking beaches, and Argen's feathers were clothed in salt crystals.

The gale was spent and, in passing, left the shore dwellers dull-eyed with the vision of its endlessly crashing water. Argen flew alone and headed out across the solitude of the offshore rollers. At a hidden sandbar, around which white water roiled, he hovered and looked down for fish caught in the confusion. His wings held him trickily balanced against the chance gusts of wind that constantly sought to upset his equilibrium.

A sudden blast of wind, stronger than any before it, hit him as he was turning close to the surface. He felt the wind striking the backs of his wings, and they, their planes reversed, provided the instrument of his downfall. He flung his tail down sharply, but he was almost instantly in the water. His crash coincided with a breaking wave. He felt pain as he was twisted sharply in the wave, and his beak gouged sand as he was overturned, and then pain flooded from his wing into his powerful chest muscles. He came up buoyantly and silently, was struck by another wave, and his first convulsive attempt to fly was unsuccessful as another wave bore down on him. He was caught again, but he rose on this one and paddled powerfully, a tiny erect gray figure in the sea's mass, sharply watching the waves that could destroy him.

Beyond the sandbar the waves were smaller and he eventually swam into unbreaking water and headed for the shore. In the big breakers, he briefly rode a wave, glissading down its side as though flying, overturned, was buried, felt pain again, and was eventually flung up on the beach. His right wing hung down uselessly. Continuing pain instructed him not to move it. He preened at it ineffectively for a moment, but then desisted. He walked down the beach indecisively, stopped, looked out to sea, turned, walked up the beach, and stopped again. Then he had a memory of sanctuary. He climbed the sand ridge that backed the beach till he could see among the grasses. Groups of gulls stood spread out across the flatlands beyond. He walked down toward them.

CHAPTER · 8

In the Marsh

$\mathbb{F}$ LIGHT enabled Argen to escape nearly all dangers. Deprived of flight, he was stranded in an environment so hostile that his survival might be measured in moments. To stay alive, he had to use an alternative to flight.

As he walked down the sand slopes of the sea barrier, skulking along some tall grasses, he looked out for patches of water in the flatlands area. Water might provide the means of his survival. He could not fly but he could still swim and this was a talent not possessed by many of his enemies.

The marsh meadow before him was patched with gulls. They stood well in the open, knowing how thoroughly the marsh was prowled by land-bound predators. Argen came out of the loose sand and shielding grasses and stepped on the harder sand that fringed the marsh flats. He now ran quickly. He was in the open and at the mercy of almost any predator and for a moment he was oblivious of the pain of his jogging wing. The dozing gulls loomed up before him, silent, eyes cocked beadily, necks drawn down into feathers. He walked slowly among them and felt security in their proximity, but he still craned his neck to look all around.

A strange quietness permeated the marsh as the wind carried the sea's throttled sough high over the heads of the gulls. The gulls were silent. The sibilant chatter of sandpipers sounded briefly. The wind veered suddenly and the surf became a mumble from the heart of the ocean. Slowly, the strain went out of Argen's neck muscles and he settled back among his comrades. The hours passed. His wing ached. The streaks of blood that ran down the dangling primaries were dark and dry. He dozed, and the earth wheeled under him in his dreams.

All at once an alarm call sounded stridently and a hundred nervous gulls shot convulsively into the air. The remainder stretched their necks very thin and sought the danger. The alarm cry was taken up generally, and suddenly Argen found himself alone on the bare expanse of the marsh. His eyes picked out the red-brown shape of a fox against some far dunes. He began running. Creeping plants hugging the ground impeded his flying paddles and he stumbled repeatedly but never slackened. He ran, and gut-chilling desperation sent his head jerking backwards in the direction of the fox.

The wheeling gulls had risen into the full force of the ocean wind and were gathering over the motionless fox. His sharp-pointed nose was raised slightly and he was looking at the lone gull. Suddenly, as the bird did not take off as anticipated, he knew it was helpless. In a lithe streak of red, he was away from the sand dunes and galloping across the flats.

Argen's running became panicky. He tripped, fell on his chest, head still rearing up and injured wing clumsily asprawl. Water glistened ahead. The fox knew that the water meant safety for the gull and he stretched his flying leaps. Now Argen's stamping feet were in shallow water and he kicked up spray and his uninjured wing half stretched out as though in readiness for a takeoff, and then the fox was in the water and kicking up his spray, but not before Argen was afloat and swimming. Suddenly the fox was in water up to his muzzle. He looked at Argen for a moment, then turned and regained the land. He shook himself and sat down to watch the warily floating gull. Bird and animal were poised in the stillness of the marsh, the question between them unanswerable. The gulls overhead were strangely silent. Then uproar broke out in the air as the gulls began screaming and the fox trotted away into the flat obscurity of the distance.

The closeness of his escape triggered Argen into a search for a sanctuary where he would be safe from foxes. Only one place in the estuary area might give such safety and he felt powerfully drawn toward a far-distant extension of the marshland, a large swampland closely juxtaposed to the river at the top of the estuary. Argen had hunted there sporadically during the early summer. It was quiet, hot, and sheltered; deep, still pools and thick clots of grasses were mixed with floating islands and sudden flights of ducks, the heavy hum of insects. Everywhere there was water.

The vision of the sanctuary faded, but the image of the water remained strong. At dusk, Argen headed back toward the sea. It roared and soughed in the aftermath of the storm. In the shallows, he ate a dead crab and worked his way north along the strand, toward the isthmus of sand that jutted out into the opening of the estuary area.

Shortly before dawn, he crossed the isthmus and trod lightly and rapidly across deep sand, leaving his footprints

beside a fox's and scaring some sandpipers into the air—
peter-peter-peter-peter—then dropped with relief into the
calm water on the estuary side. Before him lay channels,
lagoons, and open water, the tidal overturn, the estuary islands, and other familiar elements of a normal life on wings.

Once in the water again, he felt the impulse to feed. His
sense of timing told him he should fly to the far side of the
estuary, where the tidal overturn would begin soon after
dawn. Working slowly near the shore, swimming steadily
with the ingoing tidal current, he passed the shadowy silent
banks, occasionally hearing the scuffle of disturbed seabirds,
the distant bark of a fox. He saw the moon rising blindingly
white behind him and slashing the estuary in half.

The moon swung and the tide chuckled inward, and
Argen felt suddenly fearful of the dark water. Despite his
inexperience, he already feared submarine enemies that he
had never seen. These included angler fish, which prowled
the bottom of the sea but occasionally rose to the surface to
open their large spine-toothed mouths and engulf gulls and
ducks. They included cod, which, also bottom prowlers,
knew that floating birds were vulnerable and came to the
surface to hunt them.

There were also seals. He knew that they were dangerous.
They prowled the estuary and visited ocean coves, beaches,
and offshore islands during this season. Argen had seen their
black heads protruding from the water as they surveyed the
sea. Then they would disappear and he would get an uncomfortable feeling in his legs. A seal might be only a ripple in a
wave and even the sharpest-eyed bird might not sense the
animal's swift attack from beneath.

Argen paddled on. Subtly the estuary grayed, the light not
coming from any single source. Then it became visibly laced

with clouds that quickly brightened and the eastern sky turned roseate. As the sun shot a sliver of fire above the horizon and slid quickly into view, Argen cast a grotesque shadow that leaped and danced ahead of him. The troughs of waves were pools of dusk.

From the first light, the estuary pulsed with movement. The dark hurrying forms of gulls passed overhead and were gradually revealed in pink detail as they flew to stations to await the tidal overturn. A hundred cormorants lanced overhead on softly hissing wings as they concentrated on moving with the utmost efficiency from one place to another. Red-lit islands of rock slid past Argen, but the tidal current was slackening as it reached its peak. The excitement among the birds in the estuary was mounting. Young herring gulls dashed through the air with shrill cries as though seeking to anticipate the arrival of the food.

The tide rested and now Argen's swimming slowed. He was still some distance from the overturn and, in an agony of frustration, he urged himself forward with the knowledge that the tide would soon be against him. He sprawled in the water as his good wing rose instinctively to help his passage through the clinging liquid. The overturn began. He sensed the entire estuary moving toward him. Gulls hastened overhead to collect in squabbling lines. Argen was still swimming toward satisfaction of the hunger of a day and a night. He forced his way forward. The birds splayed away as the uprising weakened. Argen reached a speckling of shrimp that was spreading fast, and gobbled down as much as he could. Then, once again, he was isolated as the birds hastened from him on all sides.

After an hour he could no longer combat the increasing rush of the tide and allowed himself to be carried to a nearby island of rock. He scrambled ashore clumsily over shining stones. Forty cormorants looked down impassively, glistening black and purple in the midmorning sun, many with their wings outspread as they dried them after their plunges in the estuary. Soon after midday the cormorants left the island and cut low and directly down the estuary toward the open sea. A distant evocation of the tidal rip, a mélange of feathers, dead insects, bees, leaves, flower petals, and patches of floating sand, bore down on the island and was broken by it. Argen dozed.

His isolation from the shore made him feel vaguely secure. But even while dozing, he kept wary watch on the sky. Birds of prey patrolled the estuary, and in his present helplessness, Argen was sensitive to the appearance of any of them. A slow-flying marsh hawk beat along the mainland shore and Argen tensed with fear. The hawk disappeared, and moments later, far across the estuary, a dreaded shape came into sight—short neck, fanlike tail, squared-off wings beating steadily. Argen crouched, the disturbing memory of the peregrine falcon still with him. The hawk came toward the island and dropped lower, apparently seeing Argen, and revealed his whitish underparts, his curving beak, and powerful feet bunched under his belly. It was an osprey, a fish hunter and therefore harmless, but Argen's disturbance was so great that he was torn between crying out angrily at the hawk and running for shelter among the rocks. The hawk came on, passed overhead, and disappeared toward the mainland shore.

The sun was yellow and the light in the estuary was luminous, trembling, shifting its intensities from place to place. The distant shores silently repelled the water. Six terns stood in line on a floating branch and slowly passed the island, immersed in an abstraction of time. The light turned orange and the estuary glowed. Three identical whales, black and glistening, rose in three identical curves and were gone before the eye could focus on them. Argen was invisible among the rocks, gray matching gray. He dozed.

The tide began returning that evening just after the sun disappeared into a golden mist. The life of the estuary dimmed and left in Argen's eyes images of herons flying deliberately and slowly, kingfishers hovering like hummingbirds, sparrow hawks flying delicately, ducks speeding back and forth to mudlands and sandlands. He roused himself.

His search for sanctuary was a reaction to the constant pressure imposed on him by the damaged wing. While he lacked the ability to fly, fleeing from danger was difficult; he could not fly to food and so obey his life force. He had swum in the estuary to find food. His migration had, seemingly coincidentally, taken him closer to sanctuary. He prepared to repeat the process, and he straightened his body, stretched his good wing, scratched his head, and yawned. The tide gurgled seductively. He stepped across the rocks and let himself into the water and moved slowly up the estuary.

Soon the shores dissolved and the darkness came slyly to him. The water was flecked with fire as incandescent organisms glowed and, disturbed by passing fish, sparkled into streamers of fire. Argen swam through drifting jellyfish and heard the water whispering with the sudden rise of a school of fish. An owl screamed on the black shore.

Now that he was confined to swimming and with the moon not yet risen, all was strange to Argen. His sense of direction was not stimulated by the sight of any familiar object and he swam on blindly. When he came to an isthmus of land lying across his path, he did not hesitate but waded into the shallows. The tip of the rising moon glistened against the water. A large flat creature shot itself hard against his legs underwater and sent him leaping clumsily into the air. The primitive king crab, finding itself caught in the shallow water by Argen's approach, had twitched its ten legs and sent its domed carapace shooting into deeper water. Argen looked at the water dubiously. The shore glistened darkly and a shorebird whistled nearby.

He stepped forward cautiously and the moon threw his vague shadow ahead of him. The protective cloak of darkness did not diminish his fear of the land. But at the same time he was driven on inexorably to move into safer territory and this land lay between him and his destination. He rose out of the shallows till tiny waves curled over his feet. He paused, listening. *Koree-koree-koree*, cried an airborne bird, the cry ricocheting along the shore in a series of echoes. As Argen looked shoreward into the gloom, seeing muffled details picked out by the moonlight—a white patch of sand, the outline of a stranded tree branch—he saw a pair of lights glowing at him, apparently floating in mid-air and set close together. He looked at them, not knowing he was seeing the image of the moon reflected back to him through the eyes of a fox. He stepped out of the water and began walking up the sloping strand. Suddenly, in the distance, the air throbbed with a deep-throated owl call, *ho-ho-ho*, which was almost immediately echoed by the throbbing cry of a screech owl, so close that Argen stopped, confused again. He then saw the twin lights move sharply and this he knew to be dangerous. He ran quickly back into the water and, even as he ran, heard the faint scrunch of paws on loose gravel behind him.

The menace of the land kept Argen swimming along the shore while the moon rose rapidly and he saw the dark forms of creatures speeding low over the water. Then the shoreline curved sharply round in front of him and he saw dark land between himself and the moon. He had swum into an inlet and the land surrounded him on three sides. Once again he looked landward, knowing that beyond lay his route to safety. As he hesitated, his feet touched bottom and, in the purling shallows, he saw a moving form. He surged forward, seized it, and carried it to the shore. The crab struggled feebly and lashed at Argen with feet and claw, but Argen hammered him on the ground, got another grip on him, and swallowed quickly.

The encounter seemed to reassure him and he walked quickly up the beach and was soon among wind-furrowed sand and drooping dune grasses. Here was absolute silence, the only sound the scuff of his feet on the sand. As he walked, he passed over drag marks and near clusters of feathers where birds had been caught while sleeping in the dunes. The moon brightened, and when he reached the crest of a long line of dunes, he looked down a gleaming curve of sand that swept down to the edge of the water. Soon he was running, his feet sinking into the soft sand, his good wing pitching out to control his balance and the disturbed sand running fluidly before him. Then he was in the water and swimming and had no eyes for the dark outline of a fox's head which had appeared at the crest of the dune behind him.

Argen did not pause in his swimming but moved far up the estuary as the stars twisted and the moon disappeared behind clouds and the flat waters dulled in ethereal dusk. At dawn the tide turned, but Argen was long since ashore and pushing through masses of reeds and marsh grasses that fringed this edge of the estuary. Here, as the dawn stained the black growth green, the vastness of the marsh pressed against Argen's spirit. Even as a flier, he had never fully covered the expanse of the marsh. It flung back from the water of the estuary, which was fresh here, in a complex of mudbanks studded with grasses and ravines lined with reeds. Guttering streams of fresh water tried to find the sea, and flatlands were interspersed with many small streams which wound invisibly among the greenery, curled oddly into deep, staring pools, overshadowed by tall grasses and the reflection of motionless grebes. The streams were like arteries that ran through the body of the mud and sand, and took the footprints of the rails who inhabited a world securely hidden from the strand.

As Argen plunged deeper into the marshland, the influence of the ocean, and even of the estuary, diminished. Pine trees, stunted and sickly, grotesquely lined distant ridges. Marsh hawks floated above the tips of reeds. The compressed and wary world of the marsh skulked beyond the reach of Argen's eyes.

He pushed through a tangle of floating grass and saw a marsh wren flying low over water and heard a rail clattering. He was enshrouded. He was invisible. He was a part of an obscure firmament, between water and air, between water and land, buried in his own remoteness. His damaged wing rubbed against reeds and he rested in a still pool.

In the following days, Argen led a totally withdrawn life. He swam up small streams and traversed ridged banks and serried sedges while gulls floated overhead. He looked up and saw high-flying creatures who loved the open, who needed space between themselves and all others. Their flight kept careful distance between them and the constricting foliage of Argen's refuge. Some inborn sense enabled Argen to cope with his new situation—with two wings he was a gull, but with one wing he was some other creature, certainly not a gull. If he had behaved like a gull, he would have cried out to the passing birds and sought to follow them. But with only one wing, he was transformed from a noisy hunter into a silent wraith who, as a final act of anonymity, ignored the herring gulls flying overhead altogether.

The greatest change of all in the gull Argen took place within him. Though he was suddenly no longer a flying creature living under high stress, his bodily demands began increasing rapidly. Under his skin, thousands of new feathers were beginning their slow and precisely timed emergence through the follicles that held his existing feathers. His entire plumage was to be replaced, more than four thousand feathers, and as these grew inside him, they drew massively on all his physical resources so that at times he was sickened and listless.

His hunger pushed him deeper and deeper into the marsh, and he moved into a totally fresh-water environment where even the animals and insects he was accustomed to along the shore disappeared completely. He now heard frogs grunting and squeaking in the reeds. He walked among long grasses and saw worms and ate them greedily. He discovered populations of black crickets and ate many grubs and insects which normally he might have ignored. He found a pond teeming with frogs and learned to wait for them to appear at the surface and then spring out on them. He even learned to dig them out of weeds and mud in the shallows and so ensure an almost constant supply of food.

In surviving, he had to undergo the constant anxiety of being in a strange environment. At first, the guttural screamings and chokings of marsh herons, which resembled reed stalks in their silent and almost invisible stances, panicked him into sudden spurts across pools. Once, unwittingly, he swam close to a heron and was intimidated by the menacing elongation of the bird's body and the sibilant hiss of concentrated hatred directed at him. He crouched in expectation of an attack. After a pause, the heron heaved himself clumsily over the reeds and went beating away.

Argen lived in constant tension. The towering growth surrounding him shielded all approaches. A marsh hawk silently appeared over a pool and Argen heard wind hissing through feathers and looked up, panicked, and scrambled wildly for the shelter of the reeds. Countless times, rails and other marshbirds whisked overhead, a suggestion of wings and tails and trailing legs, and were gone before Argen's fright even registered.

But it was the night, filled with unidentifiable sounds, that most disturbed Argen. As soon as dusk began rising around him, he swam to the center of the largest body of water he knew of and, from there, listened to sly movements in the reeds. The air danced with bats and he crouched at their squeakings. Muskrats coursed back and forth through a hundred pools and made slapping sounds which he came to equate with danger. Sometimes, from an illimitable distance, he heard the koying of gulls, like voices from another life. Only dawn brought him any relief.

During the days of swampland scavenging, the muscles across Argen's chest lost their strain. The suffusion of blood which had partially immobilized them was now gone. But the torn ligaments and the broken bone of the injured wing mended much more slowly. To heal, one fine bone had to knit together. The main joint itself was damaged. If Argen used it now, it would be reinjured. But he did not use the wing. Occasionally,. as he instinctively balanced himself when walking, he flexed the wing slightly and felt an answering sliver of pain.

The muscles mended and the bones welded and the wing was perpetuated in its healing position, hanging down slightly beside the gull's body. The primary feathers brushed the water. Even when Argen found he could move the wing slightly, he still did not attempt to fly. Instead, he jumped off banks and slowed his fall with half-crooked wings. He used his wings to heft his body cautiously out of the water and onto the shore. But though he raised his right wing, pain prevented him from beating with it.

One day, however, he was made aware that the damaged wing was mending. A mink appeared on the other side of a small stream and Argen scrambled away, recognizing death in her sharp little eyes. As he ran, he saw the grasses moving behind him and then saw her, head raised high and eyes gleaming. To save himself he spread his wings and a breeze caught him and for a long and uncertain moment he was gliding. He fell awkwardly. His left wing stretched out and took the force of the landing. He looked back but there was no sign of the mink.

Whatever sense it was that kept Argen from flying persisted. The growing use of his wings strengthened the torn ligaments and muscles. But he continued to hunt in the deep seclusion of the reeds. Crickets, mice, beetles, yielded to his eager beak among the undergrowth. Skies darkened. Heavy rain subdued the marsh and it passed through the final phases of the end of summer. Reeds yellowed. Birds began arriving from the north. Rails entered the marsh, thin-stalked birds whose heads darted, snakelike, in pursuit of land-bound prey. Their calls jerked and gulped everywhere. Anxious, Argen moved into more open marshland to a small lake that was host to streams of migrant birds, particularly ducks. They came singly, in pairs, groups, flocks, armies; they came mostly at night. Argen's uneasy dozing was punctuated by the steady whistle of wings—*whee-whee-whee-whee*—squawks and quacks, and the sibilant disturbance of water as ducks landed invisibly beyond him. He walked among the greenery and waited.

He was floating on the lake one morning at dawn. The gulls were flying high overhead, remote and foreign, and he watched them. One cried out. Argen tensed. The call came down again, slipping down through layers of time to reach him. He raised his wings slowly, lowered them, then brought them up sharply and beat down. In a second, his body was clear of the water. His right wing hurt and it was weak, but he persisted. Then he was flying, low and uncertain and heading into the wind, but definitely flying. He beat the width of the lake and called to the vanishing gulls. But they ignored his cracked cries and disappeared. He settled clumsily and paddled quickly away from the shoreline.

But now the marsh was no longer a sanctuary. The enfolding reeds scared him. He started away from low-flying ducks. Herons, pacing slowly through the shallow waters, sent him flapping clumsily away. Argen imagined he could hear the surf, though he was far from the sea.

That night gull calls sounded in his dreams. At dawn he stepped out of the reeds, faced the mist that hugged the water, and took to the air with confidence and authority. Only his crooked right wing, unable to make a full stroke and bent strangely as it beat, revealed how he had survived the disaster of the storm.

CHAPTER · 9

Beyond the Bank

THE marsh left Argen with a vision of death. He flew offshore, crook-winged, and saw sleet falling solidly. He was fearful of gusty storms, always dreading an overturn. He no longer rose buoyantly and recklessly into high winds or plunged into breaking waves. He flew into snow when the sea lisped at the fall of the flakes and felt apprehension when cold stiffened his damaged wing. He flew when rain froze on his primary feathers and he landed and preened away the ice. He flew alone, and with flocks, and slowly achieved a belligerence of spirit that sprang both from the nagging impediment of his wing and from his knowledge that aggressiveness helped to overcome the disability.

He had emerged from the marsh with a transformed spirit. This he communicated to the other gulls. His voice was changed and had become harsh, powerful, compelling. It asserted itself over the collective voices of the other gulls and commanded their attention. They became sensitive to the subtleties of his physical appearance. Sometimes the slightest lengthening of his neck silenced the gulls around him. In response, they looked for signs of danger.

The crying of the gulls served as an outlet for emotion. Argen's anger sought expression; yet he was often inhibited from fighting. So he used his voice to exhaust his rage. Often, usually during or near the breeding season, he felt emotion filling him when he faced another gull, who, stimulated by Argen's presence, would become equally angry. But fighting would be needless and dangerous and, instinctively, they both seemed to know this. They would begin screaming, *koy-koy-koy-koy*, their beaks almost touching, their heads ducking with the strength of the forces within them. Eventually they would be spent, sated, silent, and after facing each other for a moment, now uncertain what had possessed them, they would fly away into a thin stream of falling snow.

But Argen, the survivor from the marsh, was belligerent when his authority was really questioned, and this made him feared. A young adult gull caught a herring in the estuary one freezing morning and was shocked, when attempting to swallow it, at being knocked underwater by the juvenile Argen. At the moment of the attack, Argen saw that it was too late to seize the fish, but he nonetheless thrashed the other gull and the beating was so severe that the young adult vomited up the fish in his fright. Boldness and determination nearly always gave Argen what he wanted. He flew upwards at an adult gull who was carrying a mussel, and so menacing was his flight and his cries that the gull dropped the shellfish. Argen caught it in mid-air.

All during the coldest part of the winter, he ranged far along the strand and out to sea, driven by anger and determination, and extended the range of his experience. The instinct to search was irresistible. It drove him on, made him restless, and sometimes he had to fight to relieve the frustration it bred in him.

When spring gales capped the sea with lines of smoking whiteness, he flew far offshore and circumnavigated the limits of the hunting territories. He passed into the world of the oceanic birds and saw odd flocks of kittiwakes on their way to take up nesting sites on the cliffs of the offshore island. He met occasional flocks of dovekies working their way toward breeding cliffs on arctic shores. He saw stray fulmars who, lost in the tumult of late winter, were drifting back to the polar regions. He saw compact flocks of puffins who, like the kittiwakes, were getting ready to reoccupy the island.

Argen flew beyond the hunting areas to where the water became the deepest blue. He looked eastward and his fear of the sea diminished. The icy air glided round him and the white caps of waves came at him in endless, parallel lines. Almost wherever he looked, Argen saw birds moving steadily north, some almost invisible against the gray water, others flying high enough to be quick-moving marks against clouds. He sensed, in their passage, a growing restlessness of spirit. He felt impelled to wander, in this way experiencing the stimulus that drove herring gulls to spread out along the coast. He roosted occasionally on the offshore island as he returned from oceanic flights and came silently in to the snow-blotched island, cold moonlight shining behind him. The dark-veined cliffs loomed up and he floated across a sea of spruces. The island whispered. He slept alone.

One morning when he was far out to sea, he felt an irresistible force welling up within him. His body tingled. The air pressure was falling. The horizon was disappearing in gathering murk. He turned into the wind and screamed his repetitive koying cry, and the wind, now gusty, answered the cries, and his crooked wing sawed the air as he righted himself. All during the build-up of the gale, he headed tirelessly into the wind and allowed himself to be carried north with it; he could feel the unseen gullery island slipping away.

By midday he felt no urge to head for land. Wind and sea were almost too dangerous for a landing on the water. The waves had deepened and lengthened. Many of them broke spontaneously, crumpled at the top, then slid down their own smooth gray sides. The wind moaned and wailed and hissing sheets of spray pattered against his plumage.

Other birds fought the storm, though few had his aplomb. A pair of dovekies passed him, helplessly committed to diagonal flight across the wind, using all their strength to stay in control of their flight. They would survive, despite their small size, for there was still plenty of sea ahead of them and there was no danger yet of being wrecked ashore.

The day had gone through sharply contrasting stages, at first lively with the passage of dovekies, puffins, and odd kittiwakes, then somber and dark with no life visible at all. In midafternoon Argen saw a small tight flock of migrating shorebirds hurtling low at wavetop level and they seemed in imminent danger of striking the water. One moment they were visible, the next moment they were gone, not into the water but beyond to the north and the breeding grounds in the arctic tundra. A solitary murre appeared in the trough of a wave and allowed herself to be submersed by the breaking waves. She looked at Argen but made no attempt to fly. While he drifted silently past, she flipped underwater and he did not see her again.

During most of this day, Argen was passing along the eastern limit of a plateau-like extension of the mainland running out shallowly into the sea. In this bank area were the grazing grounds for countless fish that fed on plankton, and the hunting territory for cod, haddock, and flounder, which ranged along the bank in search of shellfish, worms, crabs, and other fish. Floating eggs dropped to the bottom to hatch in water still lit by the sun and still warm enough for their incubation to be completed.

By the end of the day Argen was beginning to fly over deepening water. The bank had begun its long and gradual fall away into the depths of the ocean. The sea was now subtly different, darker, and its waves deeper-troughed. Argen flew across a desert of water and its motion hissed at him with insistent energy. He had given himself to the wind and in its force he satisfied his need to search and to travel. All was unknown. The sea darkened and Argen let himself down into the trough of a wave. Night closed over him.

For three days he drifted north. He was now thoroughly detached from the land and flew in a dreamlike suspension of time, eating little. The storm diminished and left him in a formless sea, no longer given personality by the wind. A group of killer whales moved slowly north with him. They rolled forward gracefully and rose to show long, sleek black-and-white bodies and highly erected fins which cut through the breaking waves and set drifts of spray fleeing on ahead of them in the dying wind.

The whales aroused no feeling of familiarity in Argen, but he had an instinctive urge to remain with them. An ancestral habit of his kind was to follow other hunters and to feed on the remains of their hunting. A fleeting unity of presence engaged the gull and the whales for a moment. The killers rose and fell; above them the lone bird soared.

Argen's instinct to follow the whales was fortified by his slight alarm at the length of his flight over the sea. He anticipated islands. He was accustomed to them in his home territory and the absence of them now was disturbing. He expected the horizon to darken as a sign of the mainland. He expected to see other birds; but the sea was empty of them.

The killer whales suddenly increased their speed as they responded to a heavy displacement of water far ahead of them. Moving as one creature, they stopped undulating and now moved purposefully, their fins slashing through the waves with clean-edged precision.

Argen sensed their urgency, sensed that a hunt was about to begin, and the food cry surged into his throat. He flew lower now, directly behind the charging mammals, and could clearly hear the foaming wakes of their passage. Suddenly one killer whale exhaled a strong blast of air from his lungs and as soon as the curved geyser of water and air disappeared, all the killer whales sank from sight. For a moment, Argen was no longer a witness. The killers had gone down to attack a much larger whale.

Their victim, who was swimming leisurely toward his arctic breeding territory, was struck simultaneously by six ferocious killers and was heaved bodily to the surface. For Argen, who knew nothing of the scope of underwater events, the sudden appearance of the whale was astonishing. The great mammal came up out of the water less than a dozen wingbeats away. Water cascaded away from his glistening back. His bulk thrust ever upward, cavernous mouth agape, tiny eyes staring, the hidden fluke of his tail striving, it seemed, to lift him clear out of the water and away from the dreaded killers.

Argen twisted away from the creature as the hundred-foot length of flesh went wallowing back into the water and a reacting wave billowed and spray was caught and carried downwind, hitting Argen's feathers with a harsh stutter. He now faced into the wind and saw a high fin wheeling and converging on the whale. The impact of the killers as they struck again was perceptible on the surface. The whale appeared again and drove upward, fell, then turned to the north. But this was only a blind reaction. The whale continued turning, so that while the killers drove against him, he was soon moving through the bloodied water of the first attack.

Chunks of flesh floated on the water. Some were seized by surfacing killers and carried down. But others bobbed around uneaten because of the sheer bounty of flesh. The food importuned Argen's senses but he was so intent on watching that he did not at first see the arrival of scattered flocks of birds. They were fulmars who had come against the wind, low against the water, moving with graceless beats of powerful wings. They resembled Argen, their physical structure being almost identical. Their gray-blue wings and backs matched the gray-blue sea. Their white heads and white-rimmed tails looked like bursts of foam.

They knew the significance of the fighting mammals and cried excitedly. Argen then saw that the northern sea was now specked with fulmars. Three flocks of several score were converging quickly. Another twenty birds were approaching from the west. The fulmars, true pelagic birds, had been drifting north from their winter feeding grounds on the banks when the fulmar food cry had been sounded by the first bird to see the fighting mammals. Their cries drew all the fulmars within earshot, the calls bounding and rebounding great distances in all directions.

The whale came out of the water again and this time showed the gashes and rips along his flanks. The first group of fulmars settled directly behind him and were gobbling down chunks of meat when the wave of the whale's fall overwhelmed them. They shrugged clear, and gobbled and squabbled without interruption.

The whale drifted eastward, leaving behind him a long noisy line of feeding birds like a composite tail sprouting in the wake of his adversity. The cries of the feeding birds, momentarily growing louder as more fulmars joined the feast, was punctuated by the solid chunking sounds of the killers hitting the whale again and again. The whale was now so exhausted that he no longer had the strength to leap from the water; he wallowed, rolled on his side, and exposed a long flipper. An almost continuous rupture marred his side and blood ran from the gray flesh in streams.

Argen finally became used to the sight of the fulmars and the whales, and his hunger asserted itself again. He drifted lower, emboldened because none of the fulmars had threatened him. He dropped down to the sea near the feeding birds. As he rose on the crests of waves he could see the jabbing heads, uplifted wings, and sudden fights of the fulmars; when he dropped into billows he saw nothing but the sea. As he swam closer, the voracity of the feeding birds hit him. They were conscious of nothing but the urge to gulp down as much flesh as possible. A killer whale surged through the thickest part of the birds and some of them were swamped. One bird had its wing broken. The others took no notice. None even took wing.

They ignored the stricken fulmar, who cackled and flapped his broken wing. But then he resumed his feeding as though nothing had happened. Argen was unable to compete with the fulmars. He took to the air and so saw the last moments of the whale, who was now floating partially awash the waves breaking over his back. His body was jolted spasmodically as the killers savaged away, but with less urgency now that their appetites were satisfied. Finally, with a gesture of his tail, the whale blew a slow and final exhalation of air and died. With his lungs deflated and much of his buoyant bulk gone, he began to sink. His heavy jaws went down first and his tail stood up for a moment and then disappeared.

With the whale gone, Argen was no longer stimulated by the prospect of food. He drifted higher till the cackling fulmars receded into an irregularly shaped conglomerate of gray movement writhing across the gray sea. Eventually they disappeared as he allowed himself to be carried away to the north. There was no sign of the killer whales.

CHAPTER · 10

The Northern Shore

On the fourth day of Argen's flight away from the mainland, the northern sea suddenly spawned islands. The air was chill and he approached the first island warily, circled it, and cried out. The cry was flung back, the echo of it sharp and accurately matching his voice. He could feel the island exuding cold. Eventually he left the iceberg and headed on north. Other icebergs passed him and a large ice floe drifted under his right wing, the black mark of a seal sprawled out on it.

The chill air, the ice islands, the flocks of fulmars, and the constant drive to the north kept Argen in a state of expectancy. He was apprehensively ready for something new in this strange sea. When he saw the northern haze turning into a bank of thick mist, he did not hesitate, but drove into it, and soon lost his sense of direction. Suddenly, even before he saw it, he was aware of a massive obstruction ahead, and he swerved violently to avoid a collision. Tail flared down, wings beating back, senses tingling at the proximity of the unseen object, he blundered sideways, hit a wall of ice, and slid down it. Before he could regain his equilibrium, he turned over in mid-air, struck a ledge, and was slung clear of the iceberg. He fell into dark oblivion, wings briefly akimbo.

Now his disturbance was intense. He flew along the edge of the iceberg and dimly perceived the difference between the mist and the sheer walls of ice. He flew higher in an effort to rise over the ice. Finally, in its uppermost peaks, he settled on a ledge. There, darkness cloaked him and the iceberg trembled in its slow movement south. He spent a night of alarms. The iceberg hissed with the sound of running, melted ice; it groaned and creaked and emitted explosive sounds which were sometimes followed by the roar of ice plunging into the sea. When he did doze, he found himself sliding on ice melting under his feet.

In the early-morning hours of darkness, the mist cleared. The moon lit up the ice. Argen could see stars. Somewhere in the far distance a whale blew and the sound echoed twice in Argen's ear. He was hungry. Having failed to feed with the fulmars, he had eaten almost nothing in four days.

Shortly before dawn, he launched himself away from the iceberg and flew with the light glowing at his back. It stole across the sea, almost from wave to wave, moved ahead, and brought the sea into ridged and moving focus. There was no sign of any life, but he flew on in growing anticipation of a specific destination just ahead.

As the orange light of the sun pervaded the sea, Argen saw a spectacle opening up before him. Mountains grew out of the sea, bristling chunks of blue solidity which, lit by the sun, turned into a series of graduated reds. Argen understood the color red, the color of the patch on his mother's beak and of food and security. The red land loomed up invitingly.

But the scene ahead changed quickly. The mountains

moved away in diminishing size from horizon to horizon, and between Argen and the land was a concourse of birds. Murres dotted the water in thousands, and he flew warily toward them. He associated their presence with food; but they were so numerous that he held off from landing. In the distance, he saw the white mark of pack ice and soon he was flying over its buckled and twisted pans pressed solidly against the distant shore.

He landed on the ice and faced out toward the murre multitudes. The birds were thrown into movement. Birds sped through the air in pursuit of one another. Others hovered like butterflies, wings beating invisibly. A pair fled past him across the water, and both birds whacked the water with their wings without making any attempt to take off. Argen looked into the water and saw murres continuing their mad courtship pursuit underwater.

As he watched, he heard a gull cry and he answered and felt a rush of familiar sensations. The company of gulls of his kind was now important and he joined a small group of gulls and flew leisurely with them toward the coast. The sun was now well clear of the horizon and its oranges and reds faded into the full brilliance of white light pouring diagonally across the glittering ice pack against the shore. Argen and the other gulls flew to the distant cliffs, uninhibited by the ice. But the murres would not make their landfall till the interposing ice had nearly all melted. Then, still courting and swinging exuberantly through air and water, they would come to the cliffs where they had bred for millennia.

Gradually, Argen became accustomed to the glistening blue distances of the northland, the isolated patches of mist clinging to islands of rock, the disappearance of the ice, the moving horizons of murres, and he felt a great sense of ease.

The chill air and the brightness of the sun were stimulating and he cried out as a group of gulls scattered around the jutting mass of rock that was their cliffside breeding quarters.

Argen was careful not to violate any territory of the gullery and so avoided fighting. He soon found that these northern coast gulls lived according to a different pattern from those in the south. As the ice melted, they formed loose-knit colonies all along the coast, occupying steep rocky inlets and tall capelands. In any direction he flew, Argen was almost never out of sight of one of their small colonies. Temperamentally, they did not have the rage, vigor, and excitement of the big gullery of Argen's birth. He experienced a growing dominance among these gulls when hunting.

As he explored his new environment, he flew inland. It was like nothing he knew, an infinite distance of rolling grasslands and boglands, still thickly covered with drifts of snow in places, marked by few bushes or trees and soggily permeated by quaking marshes. He watched ptarmigans hurrying low across the barren ground and heard a robin singing. But the landscape repelled him and he turned back to the coast.

The days were bright but tended to darken suddenly into brief but violent snowstorms. Argen's back would be thickly clothed with snow, but it melted almost instantly. He fought sporadically with other gulls as a growing urge to breed spread among the birds. He was excited by this, but though on two occasions he was tentatively courted by young females, he was not yet equipped with the capacity to respond to them. He watched the breeding passion of the adults growing, the pairing of couples, the sudden excited flights over the gray cliffs, and heard the screaming choruses on the clifftops, but he could not join the spirit of the season.

Once he was savagely attacked by a male, and, confused

and frightened, he flew far out to sea and saw a thousand puffins rise loosely into a magenta sky, their ornamented beaks glowing red and yellow. Then it snowed and he was swallowed up in the vastness of his surroundings.

His temperament, more solitary than most herring gulls, sent him easily back and forth along the northern shore. Eventually, lacking the stabilizing urge to breed, he passed from one colony to another and so became a wandering alien. The thin colonies did not reassure or hold him and he resumed his migration. Whales disported themselves offshore. Lacking enemies above water, they basked in the sun. Argen soon learned from other gulls that the backs of whales were feeding grounds. He learned to walk up and down their black backs, picking up numerous aquatic creatures which had fastened themselves to the whales' skin.

Sometimes he would be joined by small groups of wandering phalaropes, small, nervously animated shorebirds who, greatly excited, ran up and down pecking the barnacled skin as other birds might peck mud and sand. Then he would feel the whale tremble as a distant engine of movement pushed through the flesh to overcome its inertia. Argen would rise instantly. But the phalaropes always held their positions and continued feeding till the rushing water deepened all around them and they were forced to rise, trailing their feet.

The spring fled so quickly into early summer that the transition was lost in a suffusion of mist and a flurry of rains. Argen moved steadily along the coast and became accustomed to being chased by mist and rain. He soared leisurely in the middle of a cool, clear day in which every detail of the squared-off cliffs of distant headlands was sharply distinct and then, in moments, he was buried in mist and lost till he regained contact with the shore.

He became fat and sleek on great quantities of dead and

dying fish he found in the water and on the shore. They were capelin, small herring-like fish, the most numerous small fish on the coast. He looked out over a bay, its southwestern tip jutting squarely into the sea, and saw these fish coming to the shore.

A thick shield of mist emanated from the calm waters of the bay, and through this appeared hundreds of gracefully gliding birds. Their immensely long wings sent them angling quickly back and forth without effort or haste. They were shearwaters, recently arrived at the coast from a transoceanic migration which had brought them from their breeding islands on the other side of the earth. They were beginning their winter in this northern summer. As Argen watched, the day rapidly became leaden, at first patched with moving black shadows of clouds, then darkening. The shearwaters faded and disappeared, and soon Argen himself was swathed in mist.

At the same moment, he heard a rustling whisper of sound in the quiet sea. He recognized it. Gulls all around him suddenly pitched themselves wildly into the air. Argen joined them, colliding in mid-air with some, screaming in concert with all of them, and knew he was flying to a feast of fish. The capelin, all the gulls and shearwaters knew, were making their great spawning run for the shore.

As Argen pumped blindly out into the bay, he heard whales snorting in the mist, already filled with capelin caught in deeper water. He passed low over a seal who was lying on her back with her flippers folded over a bulging belly. Then the water turned silver and Argen was down and feeding on the hordes of capelin himself.

The fish were coming ashore on a front that extended the width of three bays along the coast. Almost everywhere in this area, the water squirmed with fish. Argen stood on some cliffs and saw gulls standing on a beach below him and in the shallows, all with crops bulging. Before them, the heedless capelin flipped themselves up on the shingle, expelled their eggs and milt, and dropped back, exhausted, in the withdrawing wave.

For days Argen moved through the spawning capelin. There seemed no end to their numbers. They lay all along parts of the shore in piles of stiffened dead with no predator to eat them because of their immense numbers. He flew over countless capelin suspended, dead, in offshore waters and he saw squid darting beneath him as they moved on to devour all the capelin they could find.

The bare coast melted into dark spruce forests; then came firs and occasional tall groups of pines sprouting from deep river valleys that sliced out of the hinterland. Argen saw an arctic fox watching him from the shore with an absorption that affected him. *Kawaargh*, he cried, and the fox dwindled. Finally, after another day of flying, he came to an island of birds.

At first, the low-lying mass of land ahead seemed like an extension of the mainland. But as he approached, its clear separation from the shore became visible. The island lay in the center of a large bay. It looked deserted, its gray cliffs surmounted by a black cap. Odd murres went flashing on ahead of Argen across the dull water. They headed directly for the island. As Argen flew on, he saw lines of murres moving back and forth. Soon swirling masses of them were visible above the island. Then Argen heard an extraordinary sound. It was not a cackle, not a scream, not a roar, but a massed rushing sound rising from the throats of the countless birds which formed that black cap on the island.

The sound was so pervasive and solid that Argen would have prudently skirted the island to avoid what he did not comprehend. But he saw a trio of herring gulls heading toward the island and he apprehensively joined them. The low lines of the shore rose cleanly from the sea to the black cap, now much more distinct and in places boiling up blackly into the air and splitting into specks of motion which formed into lines and wound sinuously away from the island.

The gulls pressed on. As they approached the cliffs, Argen could see murres standing in dense masses on ledges and even more thickly on top of the cliffs, and then, as far as he could see, hill upon hill of them. The clamor of their voices hit him solidly. It was like a barrier between him and the island. He faltered. But the gulls flew on and hurtling murres wheeled underneath Argen's twisting neck as he strove to see everything at once.

He was so absorbed that he missed seeing the other gulls dropping down suddenly and settling on a hillock occupied by a small colony of nesting herring gulls. Then he saw he was alone and turned sharply. He was struck immediately by two speeding murres. He tumbled, feeling pain in his wing, was struck again and knocked sharply downward. Now he reeled with a conglomerate vision of murres bearing down on him, uncaring or unable to swerve away from him.

When he succeeded in landing, the vision of the murres did not diminish; instead it intensified as he looked one way and another and saw the sky moving with their lithe black-and-white forms. He remained motionless, ignoring the other herring gulls stirring around him as he strove to see all the murres.

In the days that followed, through the north's high summer, Argen became accustomed to living at the island. The voices of the murres never stopped, and when he dozed fitfully at night, he heard their voices swelling and dying, hissing to sudden peaks of sound and sweeping all around the tiny gullery buried in the midst of the multitude. He wakened fully and saw birds flying against the moon's track and heard the spirited cries of petrels swooping overhead as the night-arriving birds let themselves down to burrows scattered among the murre masses. On some nights, Argen took to the air and heard the clash of wings in the air around him.

The herring gulls were so dominated by the murres that they were forced to fly cautiously to and from their colony. Several juvenile gulls were cut down in aerial collisions with the heavier, faster murres and flopped round the island for days before disappearing. Argen learned that a safe way of reaching the gullery was up a long, narrow gully, the walls of which were too steep to harbor nesting murres.

Gradually he saw all of the island and became aware of many other seabirds nesting there. It was truly an island of auks. Razor-billed auks occupied some green highlands at the eastern end of the island and shared the honeycombed interior of the grasslands with a population of puffins.

Small colonies of gannets were dotted, in white splashes of contrast, among the masses of black murres. In some places they had crowned small hills with white, like snow. At the western end of the island, a colony of flightless auks were established, and Argen became accustomed to seeing them coming ashore in large numbers at dusk, rising very tall and glistening for a moment with water. They looked like razor-bills, but their wings were mere stubs and they were nearly twice the size of any other seabird. Sometimes, at night, Argen heard them barking like a flock of hoarse-voiced foxes, the sound rising above the rushing voices of the murres.

Argen lived easily on the island by scavenging. The

murres continuously brought fish out of the sea which they had swallowed and half digested on their way back to the island. These they vomited up for their nestlings in such quantities that the ground everywhere was littered with fish skeletons and decaying remnants of flesh. Argen walked cautiously among the murres where they were not thickly clustered and, ignoring their wavering heads and cries, scavenged enough flesh to fill his crop quickly.

As millions of young murres grew during the savage burst of summer, the intake of food at the colony increased enormously. The island was an engine of transformation, turning the sea's fish into murre flesh and bone and excrement. The stench thickened the air, and anywhere Argen took off, his wings, particularly his crooked right wing, scuffed ground clotted with muck. He spent most of his non-hunting hours preening his stained plumage, a ritual on which his survival depended. Here and there among the murres and gannets were birds who had not preened thoroughly, either because of sickness or accident, and were now flightless, their plumage stained and stiffened with excrement which not even swimming would soften or remove. Argen saw several gannets waddling down rock slopes to plunge into the sea, their stained wings drooping at their sides, and their clumsy movements suggested their bafflement at being unable to hunt food the only way they knew how, by diving steeply from the air.

The summer passed in a sudden fulmination of heat. The young herring gulls, fledged and querulous, flew to the mainland. Argen was tense with expectation. The nights glowed under moons magnified by the season. A rising uproar grew among the murres. The murre nestlings, now numbering more than two million, were ready to leave the island.

(PRECEDING)

"An atmosphere of wariness and fear"

From the beginning Argen's life was a series of crises; he survived in an atmosphere of wariness and fear. Even as a nestling, he was constantly ready to run for safety, watching apprehensively for what might kill him. His parents, equally watchful, hovered above him.

(OPPOSITE)

"A life of doubt"

After damaging his wing in the surf and fleeing to the refuge of the marsh, Argen was a changed creature. He lived a life of doubt as he walked the edges of still pools and looked for danger among the reeds around him. Everything in the marsh was strange. All he could do was live one heartbeat at a time, and wait.

"Suddenly a murre was at his shoulder"

During the dangerous early years of his life, Argen ventured far from his birthplace. His migration to the north opened up a foreign world and his experience at the island of murres was to affect him for the rest of his life. He flew for the first time across the island and suddenly a murre was at his shoulder, and struck him, and he was spinning in the air and falling. At dusk, sheltering at the island gullery, he heard the sound of the murres' voices rushing like storm waters striking an ocean beach.

"Gulls falling like snow"

The gullery was the center of Argen's life after he had become an adult and began breeding. All the rest of his living was merely waiting to return to the gullery. He flew to the gullery in the spring, and amidst great excitement landed on the island. He looked above him and saw gulls falling like snow, crying out their doubts of a place they were visiting for the first time in nearly two hundred days. The sun turned across the gullery between white dawns and red sunsets; the cries of the gulls hung piercingly over the gullery.

"Guileful and graceful, confident and strong"

As he grew to maturity, Argen's power and determination increased. He exemplified the gull who was fortunate enough to survive more than a few years, guileful and graceful, confident and strong, sure of his knowledge of the world and of the dangers in it. His broad wings took him across the breadth of his territory, across dunelands, estuary, marshlands, tidal flats, the ocean shoreline, the offshore islands, and to the oceanic hunting grounds.

"Argen and his mate . . . alert and watchful"

During his long life, Argen had many mates. But one mate was memorable for her long association with him. She nearly matched him in energy and strength. They defended their territory at the gullery against all intruders and never left their nest unguarded for a moment. Argen and his mate stood together, alert and watchful, poised in their awareness and solicitude for their nestling families.

"He flew east beyond the gannets"

Hunting was one expression of Argen's life; he turned from one hunt to another with the ease of the truly adaptable creature. He followed the spawning runs of schools of herring and attacked whenever the fish were driven to the surface by underwater hunters. He flew east beyond the gannets that lined the cliffs of the island, the early sun rising at his shoulder, and ranged far across the open sea.

(OPPOSITE)

"Over ducks . . . and through the orange light of evenings"

As he grew older, Argen's physical powers diminished. His way of life slowly changed. He flew less eagerly into the boisterous winds of spring. As his energy slackened, he coasted along the lees of islands, partially shielded from the brisk sea winds. He flew over ducks, also sheltering, and through the orange light of evenings.

(OVERLEAF)

"The sea was close, his buoyant energy gone"

Argen's last flight was a retreat from everything he had represented during all his life. His strength was nearly spent; the sea was close, his buoyant energy gone. Nevertheless, he flew with an insistence that came from neither muscle nor tendon, but sprang from an incomprehensible force which, for more than twenty years, had helped make his life at the shore so successful.

As Argen watched one evening, adults and nestlings began a move to the sea. They flowed like black water over the rocks. The moon rose and Argen took to the air as the murres began walking all around him. He saw young murres leaping off a low cliff, smashing directly onto rocks, and rebounding buoyantly into the sea, where they swam quickly offshore. Meanwhile adult murres kept up a constant roaring as the excitement of the ocean journey infected all of them.

In the morning, the island seemed deserted with a population of less than half a million. From the southern cliffs, Argen looked down in puzzlement at the floating murres; they stretched to the horizon, a mass of birds ducking and bathing in exuberant relief at being free of the island, the young murres piping out their excitement at their first contact with the ocean that was to be their home for years.

Argen flew over the murres. They were spreading out rapidly now, swimming away from the island. He saw mist gathering in the east. He was afflicted by memories of the south and of the estuary. Later, as he dozed on the strangely quiet island, it was as though he had returned there.

CHAPTER 11

At the Gullery

FOR days a spirit of unrest and excitement possessed the multitudes of gulls at the estuary. Argen bobbed in its placid waters and felt the security of familiar surroundings. The long flight north, the return, and the ensuing winter were fading memories. Although it was still icily cold, he felt the onset of spring with an expectancy he had not experienced before. His last molts had brought many white feathers pushing out among his juvenile plumage, the first signs of his maturity. When fish rose in the estuary, he twisted back and forth over the squabbling gulls, one moment hovering with curved wings beating backward, the next moment dropping recklessly among the other birds. There was a new savagery in his competition for food.

All around him, other gulls were similarly affected. They screamed overhead, battled carelessly in mid-air over scraps of food, fell fighting to the surface of the water before breaking away. Argen watched two gulls jabbing and gouging and dragging each other by the wings and he felt drawn to the fight. He caught a small mackerel and carried it to the shore to eat and was there confronted by an adult gull whose hostile body pose, drooping shoulders, and tall neck warned Argen that he must either flee or fight. He adopted an identical pose and both gulls began a long series of calls which so absorbed them that another gull was able to dart down, seize the mackerel, and flee with it. Argen was torn with indecision and broke off his confrontation with his opponent. From then on, as he ranged the estuary, he felt sudden rages if other gulls even came near him when he was hunting or had food, and if they robbed him, he pursued them relentlessly even when he knew he could not catch them. His anger had to be vented and he screamed at their retreating fantails.

While he was in this assertive mood, he established a small territory of his own. Here he became masterful among the gulls he consorted with. The territory was not always clearly defined since it depended on what birds were occupying it at any time. Among groups of young gulls, he was everywhere a dominant gull; both his spirit and his experience told him he must inflict his will on the youngsters. Among older gulls, he was less ready to assert himself, although this reluctance was disappearing. He sought little authority on the communal feeding grounds of the tidal flats unless he was involved in a squabble with young gulls. But along the ocean beach, a favorite scavenging ground for young gulls, he was dominant.

His territorial authority was part of his maturation. As a dominant gull, his voice and even his flight were becoming recognizable personal attributes among other gulls. When he landed among a group of young gulls, there would be a stir as some birds moved deferentially away from him and others shifted uncomfortably, feeling their hostility to him but unwilling to express it.

In this atmosphere of clashing wills and personalities, he was mated. He was feeding with some other young gulls on small sea snails that had been washed up on a beach; as he worked away to hammer the flesh out of the shells, a young female stepped close to him. Immediately, a nearby gull, who had been hostile to Argen's presence so close to him, struck, beak agape and screaming. Argen was knocked into the water. He beat clear, consumed with uncontrollable rage. He rushed the aggressor gull, jabbed him in the head, caught his beak, and twisted him savagely into a wave that was purling up the beach.

There, with wave after wave hissing round them, the two birds fought so fiercely that blood spattered on their breasts. The other gull weakened but was still gripped by the inflexible Argen, who held his opponent's head jammed down into the sand and water. The captive gull was one moment choking on water, then gasping air, then he was underwater again, and his wing strokes weakened. As his opponent's resistance slackened, Argen's attacks diminished. It was no part of his instinct to kill creatures of his kind. With a wrench and a cry, the other gull broke free and took to the air in heavy-winged defeat, crying out his alarm, *uh-uh-uh-uh*.

The other gulls had watched the fight with barely contained excitement. Several had moved closer, as though to join in. Others cried in vicarious participation. The fight over, they resumed feeding. Argen, feathers ruffled and anger still in him, climbed higher on the beach and began preening. A female, the same one that had come close to him before the fight, stood near him. Then she changed the shape of her body, drew her neck in, and pointed herself at Argen. In this attitude, she walked slowly round him. He watched her suspiciously. She tossed her head and called softly to him, tossed her head again, and continued her steady circling.

Suddenly Argen felt very powerful. His feathers fluffed out

as he responded to the female's attentions, and he felt rage. He looked down the beach to the other gulls, who were still pecking away at the stranded snails, and without pause ran toward them. In one charge along the water's edge, he cleared the beach of gulls and sent them screaming into the air. But then he was uncertain and flew away himself, leaving the female alone on the beach.

This was Argen's first experience with the beginnings of mating and it was purely accidental that on the next day, on the estuary flatlands, he was approached again by the same female. She, feeling the urge within her, had been desultorily courting males for several days, but now, when she approached Argen again, he recognized her and his response was different. As she called to him and circled, he began regurgitating some crab he had caught moments before; instantly the female was at his head, gripping his beak for a moment, then seizing the crab fragments as they appeared and swallowing them greedily.

Though Argen was still uncertain, a bond was building between the two birds, and when he flew from the gull flock, the female followed him and kept a position behind and slightly beneath him as he flew inland over spruce and fir forest. He came to an arm of the estuary, glistening with mud and white sand, and impulsively landed. The female came down closely behind him. The two birds walked the edge of the water, not attending to each other's presence, but unified in their identical activity.

During ensuing days, Argen's courtship, which was a slowly developing thing, frequently filled him with aggression. But this force was made sublime by a stronger influence, his maleness, and so he did not always need to fight to vent his feeling. Here and there among the gull flocks at the estuary, the beginnings of similar pairing were engaging other gulls and there was an atmosphere of heightened expectation everywhere gulls gathered together.

The estuary was often calm, overhung with gray skies. But when the wind came, it was icy and blustery and brought white-capped waves hissing up against the estuary current. It whipped sand across the flats with stinging force. On such days, the gulls rose and cried out the ineffable emotions of a restless season. Argen often found himself leading such displays.

At first he walked up and down a sand bar in a state of agitation, and cried out to the other gulls. They cocked sleepy eyes at him, then relapsed into their dreaming. But the spirit held him. It held the interest of his mate and she stood near him and echoed his cries. He cried out frustration, anger, warning. He rose swiftly, uttering a piercing scream. In a moment, a hundred gulls rose behind him. His mate was close beneath. The estuary fell rapidly below. Argen had no feeling for it; he was absorbed in his own red-eyed rage and his shrieking cries. The reaction set up by his cries spread along the estuary. Now a thousand gulls had risen, then five thousand, as though lifted by an unseen wedge of force running beneath them.

The uproar was now tremendous. The gulls wheeled and screamed in an aerial conglomeration that extended the full length of the estuary. Argen flew above the other gulls. Strangely, the emotion that had gripped him was dying as fast as it had come to him. He was now almost silent as he swung across the sky with his mate. He looked far out to sea and could see the island of terns and, far beyond that, the offshore island, a thick blue line surmounted by white patches of snow. With these images still with him, he drifted slowly down through the other gulls. They were quieter now as they felt that the moment of display was over. Soon Argen and his mate and all the other gulls were settled silently across the reaches of the estuary.

These massive aerial displays continued for ten days and each was more excited than the last. Sometimes Argen led them; sometimes they were led by gulls far distant and invisible to him. But always, the spirit of the uprisings was suggestive of imminent events. These were soon revealed.

Argen was poised at the beginning of a new kind of life. He could only instinctively follow the example of other gulls or the promptings of his own senses. He did not know what he must do; but every time he rose in the aerial movements, his eyes sought out the offshore island, and it was there, he began to feel, that the next event would take place.

One morning, soon after the gulls had dropped back to their places on the ground, some of them near Argen began taking off and heading steadily down the estuary. He instantly recognized the meaning of this, gave a low call to his mate, and followed them. The downward movement along the estuary grew quickly. At one time scores of gulls beat steadily toward the sea. They were joined by others from the banks of the estuary and the flight thickened.

The excitement of the flying birds was now general. The gulls flew eagerly, quickly, heedlessly, heads stretched forward, bodies tense with expectation. The gulls' purpose was so definite that when a peregrine falcon arced overhead, not a single bird wavered. The falcon disappeared out to sea and the gulls passed over the now deserted island of terns. The offshore island was now clearly visible, and the flock began rising.

Argen, watching the island, beat upward with short, chopping wingbeats, for he felt fearful. The island was both strange and familiar to him. He remembered his mother. But he also remembered the dazzling flights of the falcons. He remembered the wet horror of the rainstorm.

As the gulls rose, they overflowed the rim of the island and floated, so well poised on the ocean breeze that they seemed a stationary part of the sky. All were looking down, hundreds of eyes probing among the stunted spruces and examining bare cliffs, watching the rocks where the waves broke, visually examining the island.

The gulls saw a raccoon intently watching the soaring birds, and his presence was communicated quickly by a series of cries that rippled through the rest of the gulls. The raccoon was only recently wakened from his winter hibernation. The gulls would provide his food, but till they began nesting, he would live at the edge of starvation. He watched the birds slowly drifting to the northern end of the island.

Argen now felt the need to descend. It was an ambivalent urge. He knew he belonged on the island. He called to his mate. But he mistrusted the bare land below. Even as he dropped, he cried out in anguish; his cry echoed and re-echoed among the dropping birds. But down he went, his mate close behind, and the downward movement spread infectiously. The gulls dropped like leaves.

The ground loomed up, expanded, filled with menacing detail, and the cries of the fearful gulls rang out more insistently. Argen tried to land. He swooped down but could not make contact with the earth. It seemed to resist him and to hurl him back into the air. He felt clumsy, torn back and forth in mid-air, but actually he was lofting up and down with graceful speed, his feet one moment outstretched waiting to receive the earth, the next moment folded back sleekly under his body as he rose. None of the other gulls seemed able to land.

A piercing alarm call rang out. Argen looked around tensely. Some murres lanced along the sea far away. A dozen cormorants sped north. Migrating geese appeared on the horizon. Gannets floated offshore. No danger was visible. But the alarm call remained in the consciousness of the flock. One by one, then in groups and in flocks, the gulls broke away from the island. Within an hour Argen was back in the estuary. Around him, other gulls hunched back in their feathers. The island was very distant and its image faint.

The visit to the island was one movement in a seasonal swing of events. Once the gulls had made the first visit, they were partially reassured. On the next visit, two days later, they were much bolder. This time Argen touched the island with his feet but shot up again as though the ground were hot. On ensuing days, some gulls settled but always rose quickly and flew back to the mainland.

Finally, on the fifth of the offshore flights, the gullery was taken. Argen felt confident and his distaste and fear of the island were almost absent as the birds began their escalated rise over the cliffs. The wind was steady and cool, the sea sparkled, the spruces were a bright, rich green, and now he reached out for this land, this good and familiar place, and led the gulls down, and in a moment was firmly on land and walking around it, crying out excitedly. His mate dropped down nearby. Another gull landed, his mate with him. The disorderly multitudes of the air magically disappeared. As far as Argen could see, pairs of birds stood together and the gullery was formed.

During this early phase of the gullery's existence, Argen was a victim of the community force which shaped the character and dynamism of the colony. He settled instinctively on the highest piece of ground he could see, a knoll which stood up prominently among the countless other sweeping hummocks of the gullery territory. But almost immediately, he and his mate squabbled with nearby gulls, who crowded against them, pecked them, screamed at them.

There was no actual fighting, but Argen found himself edged away from the top of the knoll. By the second day, he was not permitted to land on the knoll. As the days passed, he found it difficult even to approach the knoll as the territories of the gulls became established. Yet Argen knew he must have territory, he must have a piece of land from which *he* could drive intruders. After five days, he found he was master of a narrow strip of land almost at the edge of a cliff that dropped vertically to the rocks on the shore.

To hold this area, he had to fight, or be driven off the land altogether. His mate stood nearby and watched him. An intruding gull walked over a faint stain of grass and the sight of him made Argen's body stiff. He faced the other gull, who, with a rapid movement of his beak, ripped up a mass of dry grass. Argen ran forward and seized the grass and pulled. The other gull resisted him and the two birds tugged and strained. Argen felt himself winning. He increased his efforts, straining back in an agony of effort. Suddenly the grass tore loose and both birds, violently released, fell backwards.

The other gull rolled over on his side, a wing cocked up. When he regained his feet, his bodily stance became faintly submissive, his neck withdrawn. Argen was the victor. He moved forward and watched the other gull retreat. This contest of bluff and counterbluff, attack and counterattack, was to continue through the crowded gullery during much of the summer.

Territory was the crux of gullery life and it was complicated by the daily arrival of hundreds of new pairs who, here and there, were forcing their way into occupied or partially occupied territory. This put pressure on nearly all the territories around them. In some instances, a long series of fights was touched off, some so frantic that Argen was drawn to them as a bystander, his emotions inflamed by the savagery of the physical contact.

In one fight, the head of one gull was so badly ripped that he was blinded by his own blood. Breaking off the fight, he blundered into Argen, who instinctively attacked him. Other watching gulls joined in and the blinded gull was dragged and shoved helplessly. Finally, with a stricken cry, he flew and crashed into an incubating female; her mate screamed and charged. The blind gull blundered on, now surmounted by a mass of screaming birds whose cries reflected concern and hostility at his strange behavior. Eventually, possessed by pure panic, the gull got clear of the gound, narrowly missed some dead spruces, and headed falteringly out toward the sea.

As the gullery became more crowded its collective nervous tension increased, and Argen and his mate were now pressed hard up to the edge of the cliffs. Several aggressive males in nearby territories watched their every move, ready to charge them the moment they neared the boundaries. This made Argen nervous and he gave a long series of calls; his voice thickened with rage but was whipped away in winds already filled with the emotional voices of thousands of other gulls who shared his dilemma.

The pairs of gulls gradually gained cohesion as territory became clearly defined and as new couples fitted themselves into the complex situation of the gullery. Argen and his mate often left their territory together early in the morning to range among the shallow water around coastal islands where expanding schools of small and large fish were beginning to feed. At the nesting territory, the female's importuning for food sometimes stimulated Argen to go through half-finished motions of building a nest; he scraped at the ground with his beak and cried out to his mate.

Meanwhile, the rest of the gullery birds, which frequently gathered in loose flocks on offshore rocks and along the coastal fringe of the island, were sharing the experience of Argen and his mate. Argen saw male birds copulating with females and this excited him. He stood close to his mate among a group of birds dozing at the water's edge and suddenly began shaking his head at her. She looked at him without responding. He walked around her, half lifted his wings, and began uttering a series of harsh cries, straining them out as though in the possession of acute emotion. Then he jumped on his mate's back, slipped awkwardly for a moment, then fell when she ran forward a few steps.

But as the days passed, there was growing assuredness of what must be done. Though she sometimes pecked him when he attempted to mate with her, she soon began responding to his advances by shaking her own head. The two birds circled each other, as though in a slow dance, but this still did not end in mating. Argen's frustration during this period sent him walking agitatedly up and down the clifftop and giving such long-sustained screams that other gulls watched him and then joined in, so that a sudden knot of screaming collected around him.

Finally the female was ready. They returned to the gullery after hunting one day and she immediately began begging Argen for food. This led to a flurry of head shaking, enticing cries, circling, till Argen jumped on the female's back. She kept shaking her head, acknowledging him, and reaching up and rubbing her head against his breast feathers. In that attitude, with all the physiological processes in exact harmony, they copulated. As the moment broadened and lengthened, Argen uttered a gasping rhythmic call which was *his* cry, unique to this moment. The cry came from so deep inside him that he was not even aware that he was making it.

The birds copulated regularly during the following days, sometimes while on hunting forays, sometimes at the gullery. The nesting site became sharply etched in their senses. Argen excitedly ripped and tore at the ground and dug a small indentation. He flew away and returned with pieces of dried moss in his beak. The female stood very tall and recognized him from a great distance. He cried out his eagerness and dropped most of the moss far short of the nest and landed with only a scrap of it in his beak. He placed it in the indentation and the female rearranged it. They were both tense with excitement and the tall shadows of dead spruces moved across their expectant eyes.

CHAPTER 12

The Egg

THE ocean was an ovum, filled with the germ of life. The island was a sanctuary, surrounded by the eggs of the sea. The egg of Argen and his mate lay alone in the sun and his mate stood nearby, preening. The egg was the summation of the flying creature, streaked dirty and now become cold but preserving a flicker of life in its albumen, its yolk teeming with cells ready for expansion, its protoplasmic matter and slimy coagulation of tissue containing the formula for an exact reproduction of Argen and his mate. This egg, armored in a thin-shelled and transient security, had soon been voided, before it impeded the mother's flight. If conditions of life became unbearable, the mother could fly away, sacrifice the egg, and quickly lay another.

Argen flew out to sea. Another egg, almost fully formed but still soft-shelled, awaited birth inside his mate. Eggs poured into the life stream. The gannets whitened the cliffs, hunched down over their eggs. Puffins skulked underground to brood single white eggs. Petrels, arriving at night, buzzed and cooed underground and also brooded single eggs. Argen heard their cries at night and was puzzled, never having seen them. He flew over the offshore rocks, where cormorants, black silhouettes, brooded eggs in nests perched on bare rocks. He flew by cliffs where kittiwakes warmed their eggs in nests fastened to narrow ledges. The terns had occupied their island and were laying their eggs.

Argen was absorbed by the flow of eggs. Herring, smelt, shad, the multitudinous vegetarians of the ocean, massed offshore in schools and eggs matured in their bodies. Salmon gathered loosely after long migrations at sea and moved inshore toward the spring water reaching into the sea from the estuary. Their eggs ripened steadily.

Argen hunted alone while his mate laid a second egg. Sturgeon, waiting offshore for their moment to spawn in fresh water, leaped up beneath him, as if to rid themselves of the contamination of the sea, then thwacked down noisily. Seaweeds released floating spores which turned into zygotes; these looked like animals but they would settle and become plants. The oysters responded to currents, temperatures, and light and filled the water with dense clouds of eggs. Anemones strained eggs from twisting bodies. Mussels, clams, scallops, periwinkles, and whelks sent eggs out into the sea which floated, sank, or drifted toward the moment of hatching.

Three eggs were now in Argen's nest. He looked down at them and felt hunger. But the impulse was quelled by a stronger force. He walked round the nest, then stepped over the eggs and settled down on them, feeling their chill against the bare skin of his belly. His mate suddenly landed nearby and with a warning *ka-ka* drove him off the eggs. He walked to the fringe of the territory. This was a confusing time. He was at the edge of a new experience and felt unsure.

The Egg

The following day, his mate began incubating while he stood watchfully nearby. At no time during the egg laying had the eggs been left unguarded for a moment, and now, as the hours passed and his mate did not move, Argen was unsure whether to leave the territory or remain. Eventually, toward dusk, his mate rose and flew from the nest. His first impulse was to follow, but he was restrained by the oppressive presence of other gulls and the magnetism of his territory. He walked to the nest and settled on the now-warm eggs.

At first, his passive brooding pose was agonizing. All during his late juvenile life, he had learned to get what he wanted by asserting himself. Now, two thirds clothed in adult plumage, he had to remain still while gulls prowled round his territory. Gulls hovered overhead and he felt his neck muscles stiffening in response. His wings dropped to his sides and his appearance became menacing, even in his sitting position. A large gull watched him from the boundary. Another gull, a stranger, joined him. Two juveniles fell out of the sky and landed, crying excitedly. They also looked at Argen. The big gull stepped across the boundary line and Argen felt himself rising involuntarily to his feet in readiness for a charge at the intruder. But at the same moment, he felt the eggs between his feet and saw one of the juveniles walking along inside the boundary. He remained standing indecisively. With no experience to guide him, he could not be sure whether to attack or defend. The intrusive gulls became dark and shadows deepened. His mate fell raggedly out of the sky. In the flurry that followed, both defending gulls worked in concert, the intruders were scattered, bitten, beaten with wings till Argen was left, triumphant, at the edge of the territory, his wings raised high above him. He turned to see his mate settling back onto the nest. Neither bird saw that, in that moment of confusion, they had lost one egg to a sharp-eyed, quick-moving juvenile gull.

The two birds settled into a rhythm of incubation determined by the female, who brooded the eggs day and night except for brief forays for food at dawn and at dusk. Argen, submitting to this rhythm, was free to range widely. Everywhere he flew, he saw eggs, and he soon became an egg hunter. He pirated the nests of sparrows in the long grass on the island and ate eggs and nestlings alike. He chased other gulls carrying eggs in their beaks and found that, by attacking suddenly, he could often force the other bird to drop the egg. Sometimes he caught the egg intact and carried it away. But sometimes, despite his agility, the falling egg broke in his beak and left him holding the unexpectedly light shell while the ruptured yolk fell to the earth.

Spring exploded into summer. Argen floated high, motionless, and saw the island stretched before him, red, amber, and green, the dawn sun blazing behind him. He flew for no reason except the joy of flight and was thus a witness to the season, though, in fact, he saw almost nothing of its detail. He saw a dark stain of herring in the shallows, but did not see them erupting, silver flashes in the sun, out of the water, or the millions of females fastening eggs to submarine rocks and stones.

He wheeled across the mosaic of shore and sea, observing, each island rimmed with sparkling waves, the terns a patchwork on their islands, the gannets a raw slash of white coating the eastern fringe of the gullery island. From his lofty position, he saw the broadest sweep of life beneath him, the dark shapes of schools of smelts moving through the estuary and turning into channels that wound through mud and sand. He might never see them forcing ever further inland into shallower water till they were kicking themselves over rocks to deposit eggs near the headwaters of countless streams. He saw the shapes of great salmon moving steadily up the estuary, but he might not see them, deep inland, hurling themselves through the air, almost in flight, to pass obstacles of rapids and low falls on their way to unburden themselves of their eggs.

Days passed through quick, thin mists, bright clearing days, and bursts of warmth. Argen felt himself lifted powerfully in mid-flight by updrafts and he learned to use these, particularly in the evening, for hours of flying for pleasure. He saw squid gathering in schools in the shallows and several times, when plucking shellfish out of the water, he encountered clotted masses of squid eggs held together in gelatinous sheets. Also there, suspended in the water, but too small for Argen to see, were eggs and spores which would soon turn into tiny mussels, oysters, periwinkles, barnacles, and uncountable seaweed plants.

The eggs were laid and their destruction began immediately. Argen was an instrument of this spoliation as he roamed freely among the egg layers. He gulped down gravid smelts while eggs extruded from their abdomens, he caught egg-filled squid and herring, he flew to the gullery with his crop bulging with guillemot eggs, his beak smeared with blood, yolk, scales, and slime. His mate incubated, absorbed in her drive to bring her eggs to fruition. Even as she brooded, the germ of life flickered out in one of her two remaining eggs.

Mortality became a presence as death replaced young life. Dead eggs gathered along the shore and life fled into the shadow of rocks and nuclei shriveled. Even while the herring were still fastening their eggs to the sea bottom, thousands of flounder, flat bottom-living fish, came in from the deeper sea and began gorging on the eggs.

Argen stood stiffly in a spruce and watched a group of raccoons moving along the edge of the gullery. The smelt, after six days, were exhausted and began retreating to the sea, leaving behind their dead, stranded on banks of sand and shingle, their eggs preyed on by fresh-water fish. Day and night, herons, kingfishers, and gulls rode home heavily burdened by the weight of the smelt flesh.

Many squid eggs, placed uniformly in water of precisely the right depth to avoid damage from the sun's ultraviolet light, were moved during a brisk wind and, in very shallow water, were killed by the sun the next day.

Finally it was Argen's turn to become aware of the danger to the egg. He stood uneasily in a thin hazy rain which reduced the gullery to soft outlines of birds and trees. The soil glistened blackly. White excrement splotched green grass. Brooding gulls hunched down and the melancholic rain surrounded them. Argen shook the clinging droplets from his back and looked agitatedly toward a distant uproar of gulls. The raccoons were entering the gullery again.

Fifteen raccoons lived on the island. How their ancestors had reached the island was a secret of the past; perhaps it was during a radically different winter when the sea froze out to the island; perhaps a pair had drifted there on a tree trunk. Now, the survival of the raccoons was a constant struggle against hunger. From the moment they awoke from hibernation, they impatiently awaited the arrival of the gulls while they existed on a meager diet of emergent insects and shellfish found along the island shores.

Then, when the gulls arrived, the raccoons lived in growing expectation of the first eggs. Some raccoons died every year at this time. When egg laying began, they mounted a sustained assault which immediately wiped out all the nests along the fringes of the gullery. They had been on the island so long that the customary behavior of their kind had become modified. Lacking all enemies except hunger, they had no need to be nocturnal. They hunted day or night, as the mood suited them.

Each day, or night, the raccoons penetrated deeper into the gullery and each animal might eat as many as thirty eggs in one foray. The gulls who had lost their nests built new ones. But they instinctively put more distance between their nest and the next, so that the raccoons' hunting was less productive. This, in turn, sent them deeper into the gullery, to areas where hunting was easier.

Eventually Argen's eggs faced their own particular crisis. From the top of a tree, he watched the raccoons advancing, moving forward in spurts as they investigated nest after nest, clustering suddenly when one of them found eggs. He saw them picking up eggs, nuzzling them, rapping them on the ground, eagerly licking up the spilled contents.

Argen's confrontation with a raccoon occurred in the early evening of the following day and terminated a day of rising confusion among the nearby gulls. At first, Argen had stood stiffly while the screams of the gulls became deafening. Then he rose with them and immediately saw five raccoons working methodically through some long grass. He dived down on one raccoon. Up loomed the waddling walk, the sharp muzzle, the white-patched, knowing face. Argen screamed with all his power. But the raccoon took no notice. All around, gulls were rising and falling like bright white petals in a light wind. The raccoon picked up an egg, flinched as a female gull dived and struck him on the shoulder with a downflung foot, cracked open the shell, and ate the living embryo. The gull cries became shrill.

Finally Argen's nest was menaced by a single animal. Argen hovered, silent, watchful. The raccoon rose, sniffed the wind. Argen's mate was dead still on the nest, half shielded from the raccoon by some long grass. But the raccoon saw her and started forward. Instantly Argen dropped. Unlike the other gulls, he was silent and remained silent till he was just above and behind the raccoon, who had not yet seen him. At the last moment of his dive, he uttered a whistle, almost a scream, a cry that was at once loud and soft, almost ventriloquial, but intensely piercing. The effect on the animal was instantaneous. He whirled round and was struck in the face by a loose mass of feces which Argen discharged as he curved upward from the raccoon's head.

Now he circled, *kaa*-ing. The raccoon, baffled by the speed of events and by the sticky odoriferous mess that filled his nostrils, ran off toward the cliffs and paused there, cleaning himself. His desire to plunder the gullery was gone. Later, he walked along the cliffs to the north and eventually disappeared into some spruces.

The danger from the raccoons approached and receded over ensuing days. Each approach to Argen's territory aroused both birds to such frenzy that their attacks were reckless and repeated. Argen found himself whirling into the air at the first sight of a raccoon, poised over the scuttling animal, then falling steeply, his legs thrust stiffly down to strike the raccoon twin blows to the head or, if the animal did not turn his head at the attack, to strike with his beak. These blows were so heavy and well placed that they frequently broke through fur and flesh to draw blood and sent the raccoon running in surprise and pain.

But at night Argen was almost powerless against the raccoons. He could not see well enough to make such bold aerial attacks. He spent hours flying in bright moonlight. Gulls glided past him in wraithlike silence. The sea glittered coldly under their black wings. Fortunately the night seemed to restrict the raccoons as well. On many nights an uproar of gulls could be heard in the distance, but it rarely came close to his territory.

Argen shared with his mate a rising concern over the approaching fruition of the incubation, already manifest under his brooding belly in actual movements and, occasionally, piping cries inside one of the eggs. Their concern was given bitter flavor by the simultaneous arrival at the gullery of a number of adult and juvenile gulls who seemed drawn by the possibility of pillaging the embryos of the gullery. Many of these birds were adults who had been widowed in the various conflicts of this crucial season and were now thrown into a limbo in which they moved naturally to the greatest concentration of gulls they could find. They became sleepers and watchers at the edge of the gullery. Argen saw black-backed gulls everywhere, standing dozing on the peaks of nearby cliffs, resting on stones or among shoreline rocks, sleepily watching the herring gulls. His mate, equally concerned, paused and cried out to groups of blackbacks when she was off the nest. They ignored her.

Suddenly a large blackback was very close. He had materialized out of the sun and landed a dozen paces from Argen's watching station near the nest. Argen's stance reflected his readiness to fight. But the blackback ignored him and walked diagonally past him. Argen thus became a victim of a dissimulation he himself had used, having no instinct to deal with an enemy who refused to fight. He stood irresolute while the blackback walked toward the nest. But Argen's mate was directly menaced and was able to meet the challenge. She hurled herself at the intruding gull. He rose easily and disappeared over the cliffs.

On the twenty-ninth day of incubation, one of the eggs began hatching. The chipping hard tip of the young gull's beak appeared through a tiny hole in the shell, which, in the strain of his effort, rocked back and forth as he worked away. Both parents were alert and nervous. Argen repeatedly brought small pieces of herring and crab to the nesting site and regurgitated them onto the ground, where they lay unheeded. Within a day, the nestling was free of the egg, the shell was thrown out of the nest, and for a brief moment the full power of the almost vertical sun shone on the naked nestling, wriggling heedlessly into a new life.

CHAPTER 13

From the Nest

THE gullery expanded like myriad dividing cells. Twenty days before, Argen and his mate had incubated among forty thousand birds. Now, seventy thousand gulls, adults and nestlings, occupied the island. In places, the gullery was transformed from verdant lushness to fecal desolation. The rotting debris of discarded fish and regurgitated flesh, of putrifying corpses and excrement, combined to suffuse the gullery, on calm days, with a sour miasma that collected almost visibly in hollows.

As Argen flew across the summer sea, the island glowing behind him, he passed over a transformation of life. The rise of new populations of fish was visible; he dropped down and countless specks of life flashed in the water, scattered madly, paused trembling, and fled again when he ducked his head. The larval herring were fleeing their numerous enemies. Young cod and haddock swam through green, sun-drenched upper layers of water during their brief immature existence at the surface before descending to the bottom. The water was green because it was filled with hatching plankton, an indescribably huge expansion of life.

In the growth of life around him, Argen was a part of the readjustment in which the new life was decimated. He stood on a sandbank at dusk and watched the smooth water stirring as a pack of fast-moving pollock drove upwards among a large school of young herring. A pair of herons passed silently, their breeding finished already, their last youngster dead in the jaws of a fox. The cool and rotund moon shone on the teeming sea and Argen drifted offshore, his crop filled with digesting crab.

His concern for his youngster was a slender but insistent link between him and his nesting territory, and his attachment to both territory and nestling increased as the nestling grew. He became steadily more belligerent at and near the territory. While the nestling rested at the side of the female, Argen flew sharply offshore to attack a heron passing innocently on its way to a night roost. He menaced murres and puffins flying along the gullery cliffs. He fought with wandering gulls and often ascended from the territory to intimidate them with sharp chopping motions of his wings, every line of his body expressing hostility. *Keer-keer-keer*, he cried, and the strange gulls swerved away.

As Argen fought to keep the air clear of danger, his nestling became fully ambulant, left the nest, and walked to the top of a nearby rock, where he stood, comfortably heated by the sun. He had broken from his egg on a cool morning; he had begun walking during humid mists; by the time his first feathers were exposed behind his juvenile fluff it was stifling hot. The summer took the gullery in its grip and the gulls stood with beaks agape. The nestling hid from the force of the sun in the shade of a rock.

In the sea, many fish dropped into deeper and cooler water. Young gulls now stood everywhere, alone, in pairs and trios, and their boldness increased daily. Argen stood in the territory and watched his mate, her neck twisting and jerking, regurgitating a meal of herring for the eager youngster. She was a great fish hunter; but Argen was finding himself drawn to less obvious prey. He prowled the island's eastern cliffs, where forty thousand kittiwakes were feeding their youngsters. At least twice a day he scanned the long lines of kittiwakes, young and adult, on their ledges, seeking that moment when a kittiwake was separated by more than a wingbeat from her nestling. Given this moment, he swerved against the cliffs, seized a nestling, and sped out to sea, swallowing and choking at his burden, while behind him, the kittiwakes buzzed and moaned as though in despair.

But most of the gullery's food came out of the sea. Even Argen's kittiwake hunting was, indirectly, a harvest from the sea. The kittiwakes were feeding almost exclusively on shrimplike crustaceans which were recently hatched from eggs laid offshore but carried inshore by currents. The crustaceans, in turn, were feeding on invisible creatures in the surface plankton. Also feeding on this plankton were herring, smelt, shad, so Argen's youngster was ultimately sustained, not by herring or young kittiwakes, but by the vegetable plankton, which, in turn, was sustained by the sun.

The eggs of the plankton had hatched into many forms of life, flagellates and dinoflagellates, radiolarians and foraminifera, hatched into a million different shapes and floated, glistening minutely, in the warm upper layers of the ocean and generated a chain reaction in which tiny herring ate young shrimp, where young cod ate young herring, young haddock ate young smelt and herring, and murres ate shad, and cod ate murres, and cod ate cod.

The plankton population of the sea around Argen's island

was growing as he passed quickly back and forth under a sun reddened in pale mist. The fruits of the plankton's invisible flowering were spread everywhere by currents. Crab eggs hatched and the young crabs drifted out to sea and were carried up and down the coast, being eaten, one by one, by fish. The progeny of the oysters, most of which had hatched in the shelter of the estuary, had transformed into tiny perfect copies of their parents. Countless numbers had drifted out of the estuary and joined the oceanic plankton and were being spread up and down along the coast in a widespread but abortive attempt to found new colonies. Argen passed over a flock of kittiwakes swarming over a visible thickening of plankton which they were gobbling down greedily.

The tide ebbed and a soft wind blew from the southeast and the sea was suddenly filled with a new population of young jellyfish. They had a vestigial power to swim, but had no brains, no real limbs. As these moon jellies flowed through the channels into the sea, they clustered thickly enough for Argen to catch glimpses of their pulsing orange-colored interiors, lit obliquely by a low sun. The jellies had been launched as scraps of tissue, the previous year, from ancestral jellies now long dead, and had transformed themselves into replicas of their forebears. Though blind and seemingly helpless, more jellies than herring gulls would survive this year. Argen flew on and later found a stranded mackerel.

Most of the new life at the shore was at the mercy of the manifold dangers surrounding it. But Argen's nestling, vigorously active now, sought to improve his situation. He clamored at Argen's beak, never quite allowing him to fully regurgitate the food before pushing, thrusting, squawling for it. Argen was sometimes pushed off his feet and he pecked the youngster. The nestling's eyes dulled and he hunched down in recognition of authority. He was soon half-fledged. He grew with great speed and beat his gangling wings. Argen *kaa*-ed at him and felt the uncertainties of this first breeding year become less fearful.

As the nestling became increasingly vociferous for food, Argen and his mate flew further from the island to hunt as the sea's resources diminished. In one day, the gulls of the island brought in their crops, more than two hundred and fifty thousand slain creatures to the gullery. These included squid, herring, smelt, the flesh of stranded rays and dogfish, young guillemots and murres, kittiwakes and terns, sand eels, crabs, urchins, clams, and the bodies of countless other victims of the sea, gathered in the gulls' ceaseless patrolling of shore and ocean. Yet their harvest was tiny compared with the total catch of the gannets, kittiwakes, murres, terns, razorbills, and puffins which, collectively, caught several million creatures daily and, in doing so, revealed the scope of the season's expansion of life.

The food came ashore, digesting rapidly in the crops of gannets, murres, razorbills, and gulls, and by the time the parent birds reached the island, the fish they had caught were almost pulp, disintegrating, and easily broken up and digested by the nestlings. Argen silently watched young gannets thrusting their bodies deep inside the mouths of their parents as they took the food directly out of the crop. A murre came winging inshore with a large fish sticking out of her throat. She regurgitated the fish onto the ground and her nestling pecked at the partially digested half of the fish that had rested in her crop. The puffins, so closely related to the murres, brought their food ashore fresh, rows of tiny fish crimped into their ornamented beaks. At dusk Argen swallowed a crab, after smashing its carapace, and began to digest it. He would feed it to his nestling at dawn. Overhead, the first petrels buzzed. Their method of preserving food was to transform the results of three or four days of hunting at sea into an odorous oil, a synthesis so rich it could sustain a nestling for days. The terns caught minnows, always singly, and took each fish individually to the ternery. The kittiwakes flew inshore with their crops filled with planktonic crustaceans by the thousands. This transfer of food induced rapid growth and Argen's nestling doubled his size and weight in fifteen days. His parents stood tall and watchful between feeding bouts and he, sleepily content, crept up the side of a stone to be near them.

As the gullery matured, the nestling survived because of the bond and the protection of the family. But this was an exceptional situation among the creatures on the island. The gannet colony was swollen with thousands of young birds, dark-plumaged and still marked by fluffs of nestling feathers, who called insistently and looked with expectant confidence for parents who had deserted them. They were bigger than Argen and he sensed their disturbance and flew low over them in his curiosity. They cried out to the unresponsive sky. Their parents, a day's flight offshore, dived into schools of fish.

The puffin youngsters were also being deserted, and Argen saw the first of them, in his moonlight flights, standing cautiously at the entrances of the burrows as they appraised the night world of the island. They flapped their stubby wings experimentally. Some of the more adventurous of them scrambled over rocks and were taken by watchful gulls and so, instead of finding freedom in the open sea, ended up in the gullets of gull nestlings.

Argen's youngster was now beyond the crucial first stage

of his life and would not meet the next crisis till he was fully
fledged and ready to begin fending for himself. Other youngsters, less developed perhaps, were facing their crisis now.
For several days, Argen had become accustomed to chasing
and catching half-fledged young murres who had left their
cliffside nests prematurely and appeared in the water at the
base of the cliffs. As he floated over the cliffs in the soft
yellow light just before sunset, he saw a sharp head project-
ing from a slit in the cliffs. A young murre jumped
clear and fell sheer into the sea, wings feebly outstretched.
Argen recognized the bird, and the northern island of auks
came to him in a sudden pang of memory. Other young
murres came out of the slit. Adults were clustered around the
entrance; some of them took to the air with the youngsters,
and with solicitous cries, *ehr-ehr-ehr*, the last of the murres
left the slit and soon the sea around the cliffs was filled with
their exuberantly diving and ducking forms.

The drive to the sea transcended everything. It was a reflex action similar to that which had spurred Argen far out to
sea the previous spring. But he, being half of the land and
half of the sea, could not share the true seabird's obsession to
get away to sea at any cost. Young gannets teetered at the
edge of the great drop as they tested their innate confidence.
Their first flight had to be perfect. Argen saw them falling
from the cliffs, gliding clumsily, unable to cope at first with
the tricky force of the wind. Some turned back toward the
cliffs as though regretting their decision to fly and some of
these struck rock and bounced back into the air. Others fell,
sprawling and scrabbling, to the wet rocks. At night, the
petrels swarmed in from the deep sea and scuttled underground to feed their slowly developing progeny, still months
away from even seeing the open air.

The days became stiflingly hot and Argen and his mate

sought relief in bathing. They took turns flying offshore a
short distance to duck their heads underwater, at the same
time thrusting their wings down and cascading water all over
their backs. While in the water they also fluffed out their
inner body feathers, so that they became dampened and, in
the process of drying, surrounded their bodies with a cooling
shield. The nestling was stricken, caught between the desire
to fly and the urge to escape the heat. He flapped his wings,
then subsided into surrender, beak agape.

Finally, after a score of abortive attempts, the time came
for him to fly. A hot breeze came through the spruces. Argen
stood nearby, very tall-necked and watchful as he sensed the
nestling's desire to leave. Abruptly the young bird faced into
the wind, raised his wings, and flapped violently. He took off.
Argen, watching him beating heavily over the heads of other
nesting gulls, swerved in flight as he saw a falcon swinging
high overhead.

The entire gullery dissolved in Argen's brain into the
single, paralyzing image of the falcon. The bird passed into
the blinding sun, and when Argen's vision cleared, he saw
that it had gone. The nestling now was over the edge of the
cliff, oblivious of everything except the challenge of flight.
But Argen's attention was divided; his eyes still sought the
falcon.

All during the nesting period, a pair of falcons had lived
on the island, remotely ensconced on the highest part of the
heavily forested southern section. From there, they made
their forays around the island, out to sea, and to the mainland. They hunted with that peculiar economy of predators,
never conspicuous, yet taking a heavy toll of the life around
them.

They had kept clear of the gullery because of the large

number of birds there. But now, with so many vulnerable young gulls and other birds reaching flying age, they became bolder. As Argen's youngster struggled against the sea wind, the male falcon appeared abruptly again, this time over some distant spruces. The youngster was totally absorbed in his flight and puzzled, for the moment, by the sudden disappearance of the ground under him as he flew beyond the cliffs.

The gull nestling did not catch the falcon's attention. He was wholly occupied with his memory of an exact place among the shoreline rocks where, days previously, he had seen some guillemots. As he sped along the shore, he raised a continuous blossoming explosion of dismayed gulls into the air. Argen, still transfixed, but conscious that his mate had gone whirling upwards at the first flight of the nestling, saw the falcon curve under the cliffs out of sight, to appear again further out to sea as he surveyed the guillemots' territory. At that instant, while the falcon was lost in the sun again, a female guillemot began her run for the rocks, unaware of the falcon's presence and not aroused by the gulls' clamor. Her first intimation of trouble was a roar of disturbed air, the impact of the collision, and the darkness of death.

The gulley remained in an uproar long after the dead guillemot had been carried to the falcon's nest. But Argen's nestling was still oblivious of the commotion, and after long uncertainty turned back to the island with the wind and crashed into two hovering gulls; the three birds fell in a sprawl of wings. The effects of the falcon's visit persisted and the gullery was sensitive to even minor alarms. Even passing herons sent the gulls aloft.

The next day, Argen's nestling was uncertainly airborne again just before the falcon arrived the second time. His arrival was explosive. He cut across the gullery at such speed that only a few birds caught a glimpse of him, and their screams hung suspended in the air as he planed over the cliffs and disappeared. Argen, returning to the gullery with a cropful of shrimp, nearly collided with the falcon. He flailed away and the falcon cut downward, seized a guillemot in mid-air, and flew away with it.

Now the decimation of the guillemots became a daily ritual. They were killed with effortless precision. One day Argen saw the male falcon appear brightly in the sun, dive beneath a scattering of guillemots, and take one of them in his swing upward. He saw guillemots killed at the surface of the water as they sought to fly so low that the falcon would not have enough space to recover from his dreaded dive. Once the female falcon blurred past Argen and struck a guillemot at water level. The collision deflected the course of her flight slightly and for a moment the guillemot, fastened to the falcon's talons, cut a clean furrow in the water. Then he was caught upward in the suddenly slowed and heavy-winged lift of the falcon's flight.

While the falcons were killing the last of the guillemots, Argen's family group broke up. The nestling, who had begun fending for himself almost as soon as he was fledged, importuned Argen. But Argen's solicitude for the youngster had gone. He drove the young bird away and saw him flying aimlessly down the shore, mewing discontent.

The falcons had darkened Argen's view of the island. One day, without warning, he and his mate headed for the mainland. But for other birds on the island the breeding cycle was not yet finished. Half-fledged gannets stood on the cliffs and looked dubiously down at the sea. Five thousand gulls were still nesting. Deep underground, young petrels silently awaited their parents. The kittiwake cliffs were almost empty of youngsters, and as Argen and his mate flew on, they saw a solid raft of floating kittiwakes ahead of them.

They swung down from the cliffs toward the gray-green sea and both heard their nestling calling with affecting insistence. Argen felt an involuntary answering cry springing into his throat. But the urge died suddenly. Soon the sound of gull voices faded and the island grew smaller against the eastern horizon.

CHAPTER · 14

The Edge of Survival

THE days and nights of Argen's juvenile life stretched into years and he was adult. He shook the last stray feathers out of his sixth molt and emerged with the plumage of an adult, every trace of immature brown gone, replaced by white, black, and silvery gray.

The shore did not change, but its creatures were in constant flux; their numbers rose and fell in response to the force of events. The beaches hissed impassively under sheets of foam. Wind brushed against the dunes and formed endless symmetrical ripples in the sand. Argen moved along the shore in a dream. He felt the sting of sand and the grip of sleet and was enervated by heat and humidity. He bathed in lagoons and shook snow out of his feathers. He lived monogamously, always faithful to his mate, though after the breeding season their relationship dwindled to bare recognition.

His fifth year, a season of driving rains and speeding gray clouds, was disastrous. He watched helplessly while his nestlings shivered for days in the cold and wet. Then the thin barrier that held back his darker self was withdrawn and he ate the ailing youngsters. His mate watched. The two birds

(151)

flew silently to the mainland and left the island for that year.

As Argen acquired experience, his sensitivity to danger increased greatly, so that it became a restraint on many of his activities. He was unwilling to fly far north and undergo again the disorientation and discomfort of that experience. He avoided the marshlands, which brought back to him memories of his broken wing. He skirted the territories that he associated with falcons. In contrast, he was impelled to repeat the good and comforting experiences, the hunting of runs of herring and smelt, the clam hunting in the tidal overturn of the estuary, the scavenging after storms.

The full scope of danger had to be learned. This was a dangerous process in which most herring gulls died long before they could experience all of it. The gulls, in their ignorance, fell in countless ways. Many lost heart and so abdicated their most important quality, dying because life became impossible. Many were unable to cope with the necessity of exerting themselves to the fullest extent in times of crisis and so perished. Some were unlucky and were killed by falcons, or in storms, in freeze-ups, in gales which broke their wings, or by foxes who stalked them at night. A few died naturally as vital organs proved inadequate. Some died of pneumonia or of virus infections, or succumbed to parasites which attacked their livers, lungs, kidneys, brains. No ordinary gull with a physical impediment survived for long.

Argen managed to survive through a complex combination of knowledge and instinct, of which, ultimately, knowledge might be the most important. The greater his experience, the better he was able to anticipate danger or the location of good hunting. Finally, he possessed an urgency of spirit which impelled him vigorously into life; this was a decisive quality.

In the fall of his sixth year, his mate flew inland one day and did not return. Argen found himself excited by groups of gulls who gathered noisily in the estuary and then flew off-shore, as though returning to the gullery island. His curiosity soon sent him after them and, once again, he found himself far offshore among thickening flocks of birds feeding at the surface of the water.

As the ocean responded to the fall gales, Argen found the offshore fishing both exciting and dangerous. Few herring gulls among the great coastal populations ventured far off-shore and Argen found himself among specially nervous and wary birds who were at the absolute limits of their hunting range. During this offshore hunting, he became aware of swift-moving underwater forms which he quickly came to equate with danger. After he saw several gulls being taken down by fish, his fear of underwater danger became a preoc-cupation. The gulls disappeared so quickly they had time only to thrash a wing and let out a cry before they were gone. These incidents disturbed all the gulls and they hovered, screaming. Even worse was a near escape that Argen wit-nessed. He settled among a group of gulls one midday when all was calm and no sign of life marked the softly heaving sea. The gulls were somnolent and drifted with the current and the wind. Argen scanned the water carefully before land-ing but saw nothing. Then a sudden displacement of water warned him of the presence of a big fish. It rose quickly and grabbed for a nearby gull. The gull was an experienced old female and, though dozing, she was wary. She felt the water pressure changing and saw the fish looming up and rose in an urgent thrash of wings and legs. She almost escaped. But the fish came out of the water and clamped on to one of her downthrust legs. Falling back to the sea, the fish drew the gull down, while her comrades rose with explosive energy. Argen, already aloft, saw the struggle immediately below him.

For a moment, the stricken gull remained at the surface in a flurry of wings. Then, with a steady pull, the fish went down, and Argen saw the gull's wings outspread in the green water as she sought to slow her descent. Then she disappeared. The gulls, meanwhile, were in an uproar. As the female disappeared, a score of them dived down as though to attack her. They responded with rage and loathing when one of their number was in mortal trouble.

Argen also felt this response. He could not bear the sound of such cries, the naked sense of death; he wanted to attack it, dispel it. But he did not act as fast as the other gulls. They were now whirling away from the attack area. Argen felt himself screaming, adding his cries to a thousand others, filling his lungs again and again.

Meanwhile, the female gull was still alive, still struggling fiercely against the fish's relentless grip on her leg. The fish bit higher, this time breaking the bone and leaving the leg held together by only a thin sheath of skin and gristle. The leg twisted as the fish turned, the skin broke, and the gull flapped her wings ponderously. The leg pulled apart and she was free.

With shrugging movements, she headed upward while the slow-witted fish concentrated on swallowing the paddle and part of the leg, only half aware that its victim had escaped. Just as the gull was approaching the surface, Argen dropped down warily to re-examine the sea for danger. He had no intention of landing, but the events of the previous moments had excited his curiosity. As he watched, the female appeared, beating her wings in underwater flight. Argen veered away in alarm as she came gasping to the surface, sprawled for a moment on the water, and then flew away trailing blood.

Then Argen saw the fish appear. It swirled the water briefly and then disappeared. The gull ignored her screaming comrades and headed rapidly toward the mainland, where, if she were lucky, the stump of her leg would heal and she would get another chance to survive the dangers of the sea. The incident was driven ineradicably into Argen's consciousness.

By the time Argen endured his seventh winter, he had developed an awareness of danger possessed by few other gulls. He was the last to doze, the first to awake. He led the flights to find food but frequently returned alone from them while the other gulls, less aware of possible danger, squabbled and fought among themselves. His mate returned to the estuary and in frequenting the gull hunting grounds became reacquainted with Argen. She was not as sensitive as he and was reluctant to match his urgency to flee from remote dangers. She would circle, crying at his back as he flew away. But he always ignored her and, eventually, she would follow him.

Argen's seventh breeding year was another time of heavy rains. The gannets, who nested on bare soil, were affected by the wetness, and Argen, passing through boiling clouds of rain, saw hundreds of gannets standing erect and beating their wings to shake the water off them. He saw many of them wheeling away from the cliffs, their vividly white forms streaked and splattered with mud dashed upon them by the rain. Only the intervals of brilliant, hot sunlight saved the breeding year from disaster. Argen and his mate raised three active youngsters and returned to the mainland in a rainstorm. The youngsters arrived together the following day in a flight of juveniles. The five birds moved unconsciously in and out of each other's company during the decline of the summer and eventually joined various flocks. Two juveniles flew south with a score of other youngsters. The third got a foot caught in marsh grasses while swimming high up the estuary and was killed by a fox. Argen's mate disappeared. He became an anonymous member of a large flock of estuary gulls.

Once in the estuary, the sharp edge of Argen's watchfulness softened a little as he felt all the familiar associations of the area surrounding him again. He stood on a high headland on the island in the estuary overlooking the area of the tidal overturn, which, his time sense told him, was due to begin shortly. The day had warmed and he felt sleepy. As the tidal movement began, the sun appeared suddenly and its rays, lancing from behind leaden clouds, filled the estuary with dancing reflections. The sun emerged fully and Argen's eye was filled with its heat and the blazing light that bounced off the water. For one long moment he saw the black shape of the falcon without recognizing it. The bird had come out of the sun and then disappeared instantly into the shifting points of light behind him as he swung toward Argen.

Argen's neck became very long and thin, as though it were being squeezed out of his body, and his staring eyes were so eloquently expressive of his emotion that he was transformed. His terror tingled up his back and his limbs became frozen. The image of the falcon became hypnotic.

It dissolved into the light and became a black speck in the retina of Argen's eye. Life stood still. A hummingbird hovered endlessly at a flower, a speckled glint of color in the sun. A sparrow was graven on a stem of grass. A dragonfly was etched against a cloud. Swallows stopped in mid-air. Shore birds were silently silhouetted against sand. Argen's feathers were now so tightly drawn back against his head that his skull protruded and his shoulders stood out like large muscles from his body. Without knowing it, he voided his bowels.

The falcon was now within a hundred wingbeats of the frozen gull. He turned, wide fantail splayed down, black eye stripe glistening under a sharp eye. Suddenly all life around Argen was flung into motion; sparrows scuttled to safety, the swallows bolted low along the cliffs, shorebirds flashed away beneath the falcon. Only Argen remained, caught in an invisible grip.

A group of gulls made the first discovery of food, and their shrill cries rang out. Almost simultaneously, the gulls in the estuary rose, and so revealed their numbers. They had been collecting for hours in anticipation. Thousands of them had filtered down the shore, from across country, from out of the sea, and now formed the greatest concentration of gulls anywhere along the shore.

They rose from the tops of spruces, from sandbars, from clifftops, and from marshland meadows, and settled along the center of the estuary in a long, sinuous line that wound, invisible to Argen's fixed eyes, up the estuary and out of sight.

The feeding birds moved in waves as they hastened back and forth to be among the thickest quantities of food. The masses of their hovering bodies were an extraordinary sight, but it was the impact of their voices that filled the estuary. It had an agonized quality which contained both the immediacy of the moment and the gulls' frustration. They knew that this exceptional bounty of food could not endure; it must be exploited with savage zeal. At that moment, their voices reached Argen's frozen senses as a distant muted murmur.

This time the falcon was flying for sport. He was not hungry. But he wanted to kill. There were many gulls and they were easy prey. Thus he had selected one and had intimidated it, and was now moving in slowly to catch it. He could have made a frontal attack and seized the first gull that came within his range. But this was not in his nature. His sharp reflexes, perfected in many attacks made at blinding speed, needed constant practice to ensure instant reaction. He turned leisurely and eyed the rigid, terrified gull and felt his power, smooth and terrible, inside him.

Argen, meanwhile, was now half aware of the tidal overturn and the cries of the distant gulls were louder in his ears. He sought to move his stiff muscles but his body was still resistant. He felt suspended and remote, as he sometimes did when feeding in the estuary, when he became confused by the volume of birds squabbling around him and he would freeze, momentarily oblivious of the other gulls, even as they hit him in their careless contesting for the food. The moment would pass and he would suddenly smash his way clear of the mob, clashing wings with some and finding himself clear of them, shaking his feathers violently in mid-air. He would see the mass of feeding birds winding up the estuary, the line blurring at the edges as groups of gulls invaded or deserted the feeding line, which, always moving, wavered and turned and twisted in the water as the overturn sought new paths to the surface.

The tumult of the estuary was now at its peak and it came to Argen with increasing clarity as his hearing, the first of his senses to do so, aroused from its fixity. He could now hear the sibilant rushing movements of the turning falcon. A light breeze touched a nearby spruce and sparrow cries sounded softly. He now followed the flight of the falcon by turning his head in nervous jerks. In a moment, the falcon would make his final turn. Then his speed and agility would disorient his prey. The gull's eye, focused on the bulk of his body, would be unable to cope with the sudden diminution of the image as the falcon turned and drove at him. In effect, the falcon would disappear from the gull's sight.

The falcon made his last turn parallel to Argen; then, with a quick twist, turned directly toward the gull and did seem to disappear. The air was clear and glistening and no eye anywhere saw the falcon, moving one hundred times his own length in a second, aimed directly at a small blob of white on a clifftop. Perhaps it was the falcon's youth, perhaps his supreme confidence at having the sun behind him; perhaps it was Argen's gradually strengthening resistance to the hypnotic state he was in. He struggled up agonizingly through layers of awareness. The falcon's attack was a fraction too leisurely. Argen was suddenly free of his trance and flailing away. Grass fled under him; his crooked wing sawed madly. The falcon saw clumps of grass looming dangerously and, at high speed, he actually overshot Argen and rose in a swooping burr of disturbed air and turned along the line of cliffs. Later he would look for unwary murres and puffins, which would just as well satisfy his urge to kill this afternoon.

In the tingling aftermath of his escape, Argen was wary and fearful of everything. The incident sharpened his awareness and from then on his eyes would be constantly directed at minute details of sky, sea, and land which might suggest the presence of danger. He might only relax his attention in the company of other gulls, and then not completely.

Throughout the ensuing winter, he achieved special status

among the gulls for his superior sensitivity to danger. In any flock he was the first to cry danger, the first to fly. In the spring he brought to this sensitivity a nervous energy un-matched by any other gull. When his mate reappeared, she found herself the companion of a dominant bird among the gulls.

Argen's strength and confidence were at their peak when he rose over the gullery cliffs among a scattered group of gulls. He no longer looked for his thin strip of cliff territory. His eyes were now fixed on the knoll, the dominant territory, and he remembered every detail of his ignominious expulsion from it during his first breeding year. So great was his attrac-tion to the knoll that he dropped down to it immediately, the only gull to land on the island. He walked up and down and cried out to gulls hovering overhead. They showed no desire to join him. He was the last bird to return to the mainland.

When the gullery was finally occupied, Argen was faced with a series of crises as older and more experienced gulls, who had nested on the knoll for years, contested his intru-sion. Days of threats and cries were punctuated by brief but violent battles as the gulls sought instinctively to reapportion the territory among themselves. Eventually, because of his great determination, Argen established authority over the crest of the knoll. His mate, anxious during all the squab-bling, also became part of this territory. Argen looked out over the burgeoning greenery, the rolling hillocks, the dead spruces, to the bright blue line of the sea, and felt his power.

All during this breeding season, he was filled with rage at the slightest intrusion of his territory on the ground and even menaced birds flying low overhead. His mate did not share his exaggerated concern for territory and his deep sensitivity to danger, and he would cry out to her agitatedly. She might see the danger but judge it too distant to be a threat and would preen while Argen fussed and *kaa*-ed his concern.

Despite Argen's tension, it was a successful year; the two birds raised three nestlings again, their fifteenth, sixteenth, and seventeenth chicks. When they were freed from the gullery, they expressed their feeling of release in high flying, usually over the island. They could see the gullery spread out in speckled detail, patched by groups of gulls who were waiting their chance to pillage or who had flocked together because of their failure to breed successfully. The gannets were a white slash mark along the eastern shore and the sea moved in parallel lines under the endlessly wheeling birds.

At their high aerial station, the two gulls glided back and forth silently in mute involvement in their flight and watched the limitless space and spectacle all around them. They were closer to the clouds than to the tiny island below, and they saw everything in lofty perspective—hordes of kittiwakes hovering in clouds at the cliffs, gannets firing themselves away from the land and out to sea, groups of murres drawing straight black lines across the water as they returned to the island, and, occasionally, the fast chopping flight of the falcon passing far below. The falcon ignored them, or perhaps did not see them, and gradually Argen's delight at high flying overcame some of his anxiety at the sight of the bird.

The sky became a blue dome, decorated with a patchwork of fleecy clouds that hovered low over sea and island. Soon after midday, Argen was flying just below the first layer of clouds, his mate slightly above him. They were drifting aimlessly, the island turning under them, the horizon tilting silently. Argen felt supreme comfort, released from his former rages and suspicions. He was so high he could see the mainland and the island of terns. He drifted down toward the island of terns and then swept gracefully into the breeze toward the gullery island and was dazzled by the sun smashing upward from the water. He could see the form of his mate, still circling very high. As he looked, a black speck dropped diagonally down through an overhanging cloud, and while his eyes widened and glittered with intensity, it struck his mate and curved upward and away to the north.

But Argen did not watch the falcon. He saw only the spread-winged form of his mate, turning over and over as she fell to earth. Behind her, a burst of feathers hung in the air, like a small cloud themselves. Argen was now pumping urgently toward the island, dropping down as he followed his mate's steady fall. As the falling gull neared the earth, she seemed momentarily alive as her wings caught the uprushing air and caused her body to hang down between the wings, themselves pointed upward; but then the illusion of life ended and the tumbling began again.

Argen lost sight of the gull as she fell against the sun's reflection from the sea and when he flew beyond it she had disappeared. He did not see her drop into the spruce woods at the western fringe of the island. He flew up and down inquiringly. His mewing cries brought no response.

His close attachment to the island, fostered by his association with his mate and the success of their breeding, was now broken. The following day, he drifted away and spent long hours floating alone on the sea, his tiny white form rising and falling in the serene energy of waves coming out of the east.

CHAPTER 15

The Sea Hunt

In the ninth year of his life, Argen was at the summit of his physical powers. He was sleekly sheathed in feathers that glistened in the sunlight and his eyes were clear and bold. His beak had long since lost its horn color and was now yellow with a bright red patch at the end of the bottom mandible. Gradually, his power and determination had confirmed him as a dominant gull among the thousands of birds at the estuary. His cry was recognizable and known by most of the gulls. It represented authority and experience and was heeded on all occasions.

He was lean, dangerous by disposition, yet he had become pacific now among his fellows. The other gulls so well recognized his authority that they contested him only if they became desperate to prevent him from intruding on their territory or stealing their food. Argen felt secure and powerful. His violent assertive rages had subsided into impassive appraisal of the world around him. When he fought he did so briefly and violently.

The memory of his mate dulled; their first meeting, the

fight for territory at the gullery, the first egg, all clouded in the passage of time and the vitality of the present.

At nine, he had outlived most of his contemporaries. Forty thousand gulls had hatched out with him nine years before; now fewer than one hundred were still alive. Of these, only about thirty lived at the estuary; the rest were spread out along the coast. Argen and his surviving comrades formed the hard core of experience that influenced the lives of the younger gulls. He often hunted and ate alone. But when he found a surfeit of food, his cries drew other gulls to the feast.

With the passing years, his knowledge of the possibilities of hunting grew immensely. When the brant geese invaded the estuary to feed on the submarine eelgrass, Argen knew where their infirm or dying might be found and he would become a silent and watching presence, awaiting the death of his prey. He knew that some fish, particularly skate, sometimes became stranded during storms. Some of his best winter hunting was along the ocean beach during blizzards, when he came on stricken seabirds and killed them.

However, his knowledge of hunting was greatest when it came to herring. He caught herring at all stages of their lives, from those so small that twenty of them scarcely filled his crop up to those so large that it took him an hour to swallow one completely. He caught them in the estuary when, young and almost boneless, they flocked together in great swarms and were often brought to the surface in tidal rips and currents. He caught them far offshore as, much larger and maturing, they prowled the areas where currents brought together collections of plankton. His greatest catches were made during the spring and early summer, when, in large schools, they headed for shallow water to spawn on the sea bottom.

No spawning run ever resembled another, for the herring were subject to infinite variations of currents, temperatures, and predators. But Argen had developed an awareness of the ideal times and conditions for herring to be moving. This knowledge, in conjunction with his ceaseless patrolling of shore and sea, often led him to successful hunting.

In the spring of his ninth year, he was mated in the estuary before the snow had gone from the hills. The female was part of the winter flocks there and Argen had been aware of her as an individual since the late fall. But ten days after the mating bond had been formed, she disappeared one night. He never saw her again. For a time, he was a lone hunter, estranged from the purposeful activity of the gull community.

He flew alone and saw gray seas bursting into lines of whiteness. He flew in light mist and heard, for the first time that season, the whisper of a school of fish rising and breaking the surface. But he could not find them. He flew among hundreds of excited gulls who, like himself, felt the imminence of new events. He drifted east toward the offshore island, where, experience told him, thousands of gulls were gathering. The air was filled with expectation. The snow ran down the mainland hills and swelled the estuary river; the estuary island echoed to the sounds of migrant landbirds; the wind-swept sky was suddenly spotted with northward-moving hawks.

As he was drifting offshore one morning, the mainland a distinct gray line to his right, the water rippled beneath him; he let himself fall. Even as he dropped, the water seethed with fish and he struck into a mass of them. He half flew, half swam, as he gulped down fish. He gargled out the food cry, which, picked up by one gull, was relayed, picked up, flashed

(165)

across the sea in an ever-widening circle round the feeding
Argen. Gulls poured into the hunting area, drawn from the
gullery island and from offshore rocks and from the estuary.
By the time Argen had gorged himself the gulls were spread
noisily across the water. Argen remained floating, stuporous,
his neck bulging with herring.

Deep beneath him, a group of dogfish, which were keeping
the herring pressed against the surface, were themselves becoming engorged as they desultorily attacked the lower
layers of the school. The sun emerged from a gray cloud.
The water twinkled and late-coming cormorants and murres
hastened to the feast. The herring army rolled on, millions of
fish responding to the pricking stimulus of the attackers with
sudden panicky flights but never changing their steady
progress up the coast.

At length, Argen's digestion dealt with some of the food
he had swallowed and he took off and turned toward the
feeding birds now distantly north of him. A lone gannet flew
overhead, saw the herring, cried out, circled downward in
tight spirals, then pierced the water in a long diagonal dive
that struck up a gout of water. Argen glided, high enough to
see the response to the cry, a thickening of gannets over the
distant gullery island as birds rose toward the sound of food.
As Argen circled, they came sweeping effortlessly past him
on their six-foot wings and formed a canopy over the herring
from which birds fell like missiles. As the gannets pierced the
water, foam spread. Gulls, murres, and cormorants hurried
from the attack area to escape being struck down, and Argen
hovered high in the air, a witness.

The climax to the collision between the birds and the fish
came when the herring at the northern end of the school
found a free passage through the dogfish. They began a

streaming flight to the depths. Argen could see their silvery bulk dying in the water; the last fish disappeared into the gloom and the sea was silent. The gannets slowly spread out. Some flew in steady circles. Others floated and their white bodies stood out on the dark-blue sea. Long before Argen reached the estuary, the attack area was empty.

Argen uttered his food cry automatically when he found a run of fish. But in other hunting he seemed to be more secretive, particularly in the fall, when all the uncertainty of winter was imminent. One fall, he found a nearly dead black duck huddled in the upper estuary and he floated among grasses at the fringe of some sedges, awaiting the duck's death. When it came in a flurry of convulsive wingbeats, he moved forward cautiously. Gulls flew overhead, watching him, but they did not see his prey. He probed in the grasses, seized the duck's limp neck, and began tugging at it.

But instead of pulling the body into clearer water, he worked it steadily through the reeds toward the land till he was among some shrubbery behind the sedges. There, with the wind hissing softly in nearby spruce tops, he began feeding. His heavy beak cut the flesh away from the bones till he was so engorged he could eat no more. He flew sluggishly back to the water and rested on it. Later, when he had digested the meal, he returned to finish the duck. But some land-bound predator had found his prize and nothing remained but a scattering of brown feathers.

During his early years of hunting, Argen was frustrated by prey he could see but not catch. Young fish darted downward beyond the plunge of his beak. Shellfish, usually mussels, lay tantalizingly in view at low tide but out of reach, though he ducked his head so far down that his tail flipped high into the air.

Equally frustrating was his natural impulse to dive into water from a height. Usually, on seeing a fish, he dropped straight down and hit the water asprawl, his neck and beak sharply inclined toward his prey, his feet held flexed against his belly, his wings crooked in an attitude that partially braked his fall. At the last moment, he flung his head downward and so struck the water. He never penetrated the surface with all of his body.

Gradually, during his early hunting years, his diving became more precipitate, the plunges of his head more impetuous. One day, in an unsuccessful dive after a small fish, he found himself completely underwater. The fish was still visible. He shrugged his wings and drove himself down, but the fish flitted away and, hurriedly, Argen resurfaced and remained floating for a moment. He soon discovered that he could dive quite deep and remain underwater long enough to recover dead fish, to rip up shellfish from the bottom, or to probe among seaweed for crabs or snails.

He flew along the northern coast now and watched the shallows where small fry teemed in inlets and shellfish clustered in the lee of rocks and where seaweed hung down blackly into the heaving water. He felt the urge to dive when he saw a group of fish swimming under him, but when he landed they had disappeared. Then he saw other creatures in the shallow water; distorted by the rhythmic pulse of the waves, they seemed to him to be moving. He lifted himself a wingbeat from the water, dropped head-first, and was then underwater and heading for the bottom.

The creatures were urchins, brittle-spined, spherical echinoderms, working slowly over rocks as they scraped away at the algal growth. Argen had often eaten them when they were driven ashore or, less frequently, exposed by very low tides. In two shrugging wingbeats, he was among them. He seized one and surfaced.

He immediately headed for the shore as he responded to the stimulus produced by having a creature between his mandibles. Instinct told him to take the urchin ashore and eat it. Knowledge told him to rise and drop its shelled body to the rocks. He did so. The urchin burst. Its intestines and gonads bulged and suddenly Argen was not alone. Another gull had settled nearby and was watching him intently. He sensed that her interest was in the urchin; he swelled his neck menacingly. But she did not move and continued watching steadily. He dug his beak among the green spines and smashed plates and gulped down the rich body flesh. Then, with increasing zeal, he broke up the last of the spiny covering and extracted the residual contents. As he ate, the female walked toward him and importuned with a gesture of her body. Argen was momentarily disarmed. He fed her with gulping motions, the urchin so quickly transferred from sea to air, from air to gull, and from gull to gull that it seemed a predetermined chain of events.

The encounter with the female troubled Argen and he flew along the coast. She fell behind him and eventually disappeared. But later, on the tidal flats where Argen gathered with other gulls, she reappeared and importuned him again and he fed her. He felt powerful and aggressive now. When another gull settled near him, he menaced him, then attacked him, and the encounter ended in a violent interchange of wingbeats and hammering beak blows. Over ensuing days, Argen became mated to the female and they flew together.

The female's personality was distinct and Argen found himself influenced by its strength. He followed her, one evening, to some tidal flats high in the estuary, beyond the thickest eelgrass meadows, in an area he had not before hunted. The female settled confidently and awaited his arrival. Then, at the edge of the water, she began moving her feet up and down, as though walking, but without moving from the spot. Argen watched her as her walking movements quickened. Then he found himself stamping the sand in imitation. As he did so, the female stepped out of the mess of puddled sand, mud, and water and peered down. Three quick jabs of her beak disposed of some creatures, then she resumed her stationary walking in a new position. Argen now stopped paddling himself and looked down. Clearly visible were two writhing worms. Argen seized one. The connection between the paddling and the prey was now clear and the two birds worked away at the shoreline till night overtook them.

The female gull flew with him, one wingbeat behind him when they hunted herring, wing tip to wing tip in offshore flights. She eyed him with intensity and concern and cried out frequently, as if expressing the emotion of their pairing. On occasion she even fought male gulls as she responded to the stimulus of the mating that lay just ahead of her. Argen felt her presence at all times and the bond between them was strong.

When the time came for them to fly to the gullery, Argen felt himself tensing in readiness for occupying his territory. He was a dominant gull and to assert his authority was natural. But he had never before flown to the gullery at this time. The two birds rose over the whispering cliffs and the green gullery rolling beneath them. There was the knoll and Argen felt anxious. The knoll was well occupied with nesting gulls; his territory was flanked by two nests with females incubating eggs on both. He hovered, uncertain, and his mate cried out.

But the earth drew him down. He landed on the crest of

the knoll with his mate close behind him. He was surrounded by the tall necks of watchful gulls. A gull dropped out of the sky and walked toward Argen. His attitude was menacing, and even as he walked, he cried out angrily. A second gull landed behind Argen and suddenly the fight began. Argen was seized by the wing and dragged. He recovered, grabbed one gull by the beak and twisted him to the ground. He saw his mate, who had taken off, hovering overhead.

But Argen's determination to occupy his familiar territory prevailed. The hostility of the other gulls waned over ensuing days as they became accustomed to his presence. He and his mate were able to begin nesting. With the territory thoroughly theirs, both became active defenders of it. This made them formidable. One of the male gulls who had contested Argen's arrival and who held territory on the northern side of the knoll was periodically concerned by the proximity of this aggressive gull and his mate, and he walked up and down the boundary region, uttering warning cries. Argen and his mate recognized that this was a challenge to their territorial integrity and they watched closely.

Finally, when the gull had stimulated his courage enough, he crossed the boundary. Argen, aloft, saw the movement, saw his mate walking toward the intruder, and joined her a moment later. Side by side, they advanced till they were a wingspan from the gull. Then, in unison, they rocked their heads forward and down, almost to the ground, and at the same time uttered deep-throated gargling noises. The rhythm, the unison, and the strange power of the concerted motion were compelling. The intruder reacted as though he had been attacked physically. He jolted to a halt. Then, as the two birds advanced a step and kicked at the turf, he

stepped back, then turned and ran deep into his own territory. Argen felt a new security at the nesting site. He fed his
mate and they flew offshore to hunt together.

She was now the most familiar gull of his life. He was able
to recognize her instantly from great distances even though
she might be one bird amid a large mass of wheeling gulls.
Soon he recognized her by subtler details, the carriage of her
body, the attitude of her neck, her distinctive walk, her deep-
stroked wingbeats. Most of all, he learned to recognize her
voice among thousands of other gull voices, from her soft,
almost inaudible signals of warning to harsh screaming.

He was sensitive to all the meanings of gull calls and responded only to those which exactly concerned him. He
brooded the nest and felt warm and secure; he turned his
head back along his body, and slept. Gulls swept low overhead, screaming, but he did not open an eye. Two gulls
fought savagely nearby, but the squabble did not arouse him.
A female gull hovered over him, uttering an importuning
cry, but he slept on. Far in the distance, a gull brought a
mussel to the island shore and dropped it. There was a shrill
clamor as other gulls competed for the catch. Their cries half
aroused Argen and he opened one sleepy eye but almost
immediately returned to sleep. The voices of the gullery rose
to an uproar, faded to near quiet, then surged into clamor
again.

At the peak of the noise, Argen wakened fully and his
feathers tightened against his body. Among that welter of
voices he had heard one small cry. His mate was returning
from the sea and this cry activated him, this cry alone.

The urge to brood was strong in him this season and sometimes he became impatient and walked around his incubating
mate, mewing expressively. When she did not respond, he

tried to push her off the eggs, butting her with his wing shoulder. Then she rose, wings lifted in protest, and stepped clear and looked down in puzzlement as Argen settled rapidly and contentedly on the warm eggs.

The rhythm of incubation became established. The female brooded all night and Argen relieved her as soon as he returned with a full crop from his dawn hunting. Then she was free till mid-morning, when, her own crop full, she returned from the estuary and resumed her place on the nest. She remained there till mid-afternoon. Argen, who had not troubled to hunt, resumed his place and remained on the nest till early evening, when the female began her nighttime vigil.

In his free times, with the hunting easy, Argen watched other creatures exploiting the beneficent sea. He stood on the clifftops near the sprawling gannetry and looked down on an oceanic amphitheater speckled with ten thousand seabirds. A murre appeared close inshore. His slender neck and beak and dark color made him almost invisible against the dark water. Argen saw his white markings briefly as he dived, but then lost sight of him as he went down, wings beating powerfully. The murre descended steeply and heard the movements of numerous fish beneath him, and, in the distance, the thudding sounds of gannets striking the water. On his previous dive he had seen a small group of herring, but they had eluded him as his supply of air had run short. Down he went again, down from the opalescent green of the surface, down through quivering stratified shafts of light, down to where the influence of the surface faded and the water pressed darkly against his body. The murre's long, slender neck was stretched out eagerly.

Argen dozed; the gannets moved against banked masses of cloud; the murre reached the bottom, a hundred wingbeats from the surface. It was gloomy and no fish were visible anywhere along the sandy expanse. The murre swam close to the bottom, saw a black form ahead, and swerved toward it. The lobster shot away in a series of rapid contractions of its tail and the murre passed on. He kept looking upward in an effort to catch a glimpse of fish against the light of the surface. A cluster of dark forms showed and he drove upward powerfully. The herring flicked upward, and a moment before they would have rippled the surface, two gannets smashed down and came shooting into the water in a streaming cascade of bubbles, each gripping a herring. The murre, undeterred by the gannets, quickly caught two of the panicky fish who were now diving to escape the danger from above. Argen, briefly watchful when he saw the gannets dive so close to the shore, saw the murre surface.

Argen saw the murre dive again but never knew that the lithe dark bird did not resurface. On his final pursuit of the elusive herring and within sight of his prey again, he was briefly aware of a large body behind him, a massive displacement of water, and then he was the hunted and was flying desperately for the surface. But the cod, fifty times his weight, seized and crushed him in flight and left one primary feather suspended in the dusky water as he surged on out of sight.

The sea hunting was different each year. Argen feasted on herring but his pursuit of them was always being refined by experience. During his early years of hunting, he was purely an opportunist. He hastened to herring runs already found by other gulls. He chanced on sudden uprisings of the fish. This was a learning period and during it Argen became aware that anticipation was the secret of the best hunting. He noticed that small fish often appeared at the surface when

murres or puffins were in the water around him. He learned
to associate their diving with the appearance of herring at
the surface. He could not see the underwater events; but he
came to know precisely when the fish might be driven up into
his reach.

Sometimes this hunting yielded a great surfeit of food. In
the early summer of his tenth year, he rode a heavy ocean
swell. The gray island cliffs rose behind him. The gannets
were far out to sea, fishing. A few cormorants were black
motionless marks on their rocks. The gullery was quiet. The
sun beat warmly on Argen's plumage and he felt sleepy. But
he became alert as puffins began gathering on the water some
distance offshore. At first there were only a few hundred, but
then Argen saw scores of them tumbling out of the rocks and
burrows along their part of the island. Soon several thousand
of them stretched out silently across the moving ridges of
water.

Argen had heard no food cry, no signal passing among the
puffins, but he sensed that hunting was about to begin. Even
as he flew toward the puffins, he saw odd birds ducking out
of sight. Underwater, the collision between herring and
puffin was creating a turmoil of swimming birds and fleeing
fish. The puffins, now diving in droves, swam to the bottom
and made their attack runs upward. The herring school,
nearly as long as the nearby island, responded by rising to
the surface, their dread of puffins being greater than their
fear of the surface.

As he waited, the water around Argen became alive with
herring. He screamed joyfully. Gulls rose thickly from the
island, black marks against fleecy clouds, and the puffins kept
coming up through the panic-stricken fish, surfacing, pound-
ing wings and feet on the water as they took off and drove

toward the island with their victims trailing from their beaks. Their attacks kept the herring at the surface till every puffin, every gull, and eventually almost every other seabird on the island was sated. By evening the herring had disappeared to the north and Argen, barely able to fly, floated, neck bulging.

The ocean teemed with herring. They made the seabirds fat and helped put Argen's three youngsters into the air. The bodies of herring, bitten and mangled, littered the face of the island, dropped heedlessly by hunters who had a surfeit of food when herring were plentiful. Argen passed through the middle of the summer in a state of well-being; for long hours he and his mate dozed, crops and guts filled with digesting herring.

Later, in the dry decline of summer, the herring disappeared and the two gulls turned to other hunting. For years, Argen had been aware of the night arrival of the petrels at the gullery island, and often, while he was aloft, the air around him was filled with the sound of their chuckling calls. He had heard the excited cries of other gulls hunting the petrels; but he had not been a petrel hunter himself. One night he and his mate stood at the top of the cliffs at the southern end of the island and as the moon rose saw black forms flitting against its face. The petrels were all around the two gulls and their calls moved back and forth over their heads. The petrels seemed to see poorly. Argen heard wings whispering against boughs and brushing through grasses. One petrel struck the side of Argen's head, and with a quick jerk of his beak, he seized the bird. Its long wings slashed the air and he rapped the creature on the ground, squeezed a gasp out of it, and swallowed. His enormous gut had diffi-culty coping with it, but after a struggle he got the bird down. His mate was darting above him, hovering like a

butterfly and lunging as she sought to catch petrels in mid-
air. She finally succeeded and fell near him to swallow her
catch. That night Argen found he could capture petrels high
in the air as they hovered, or on the ground as they struggled
through long grass, or among spruce foliage as they blundered along the chancy route to safety underground. In the
morning he stood on a rock among a score of other gulls,
who periodically regurgitated compact pellets consisting of
the bones of petrels slain and eaten the night before.

Argen's mate disappeared shortly after they returned to
the mainland; he did not see her again till the following
spring. He awoke from a doze; gleaming sheets of water left
by the retreating tide surrounded him. He saw a gull picking
her way slowly through a shallow pool and in a moment
recognized her. His mate had returned.

This year, slight changes in offshore currents moved many
of the herring away from the area of the gullery and Argen
found himself flying far up the northern coast in pursuit of
their spawning schools. With his mate securely placed on her
nest, he began turning to other hunting.

For years he had desultorily scavenged the cormorant
rocks near the offshore island, picking up scraps of fish, odd
eggs, and, occasionally, untended nestlings. But this year he
felt the impulse to stay at the cormorantries while his mate
incubated. He remembered that, two years before, a sudden
fall of rock had scared all the cormorants off their nests. He
had recovered his composure before the cormorants did and
had pillaged a nest.

He flew lazily offshore and turned back and forth against a
firm sea wind and saw light sparkling on endless prisms of
water. The dark mass of rock which housed the main cormorantry loomed up ahead of him. It was precipitous, every side

(177)

so sheerly swept from sea to summit that not even a kittiwake could find a foothold. The top of the rock, almost perfectly flat, was verdant, made so by thousands of generations of nesting cormorants. The debris of their occupancy had collected on the rock, and humus had eventually been created and grass had grown and soil had been built up. In places the cormorants were densely packed together, loosely conglomerated elsewhere, so that their occupancy was a patchwork affair, black staining the thin greensward.

Argen was poised now over the cormorantry, which, unlike the gullery or the gannetry, was almost completely silent. The black birds flashed down and away from the cliffs with a facility that belied their clumsiness on land. Argen flew to the northern end of the rock and settled. He was aware of one crucial fact about the cormorants. They responded to the alarm calls of gulls. Like some other shorebirds, particularly ducks, they tended to rely on gulls to warn them of danger, as they were slow to appreciate it themselves. Argen waited.

The wind riffled his feathers. The lines of sea came steadily toward him and their sparkling white caps died unseen and unheard at the base of the cliffs. He relaxed slightly and dozed, but he felt tension building up among the cormorants. The tension was a compound of pressures. One was *his* mute presence. Another was the expectation of food, as they awaited the return of the cormorant hunters. Another was the absence of the many cormorants away from the rock hunting.

The tension mounted. Cormorants anxiously craned necks and turned around on their eggs as they sought danger. Argen was now fully wakeful as he responded to the rise in tension. The bright sea dulled as a dark cloud obscured the sun and with a scream Argen rose from the rocks. His cry was electrifying. It sank into the ears of the cormorants with a thrill of despair and, obedient and blind, they took to the air to escape, at any cost, from the danger that had been signaled. Some fled with such haste that they kicked eggs and nestlings clear of their nests. Argen saw a nestling falling down the cliffs but ignored it and turned back sharply. The cormorants, flat and heavy in flight, were now swinging clear of the rock. Some, realizing the deception, were already braking and straining to turn their headlong flight.

Argen leisurely swallowed a cormorant nestling and was standing over an egg when cormorants came flashing low over his head and landed clumsily all around him. He withstood the menacing lunges of the female whose egg he stood astride of, and when her blind courage had subsided into alarm, neck writhing, wings half raised, as she watched helplessly, Argen rapped the egg on a rock and swallowed shell and embryo in a few quick gulps. Before night came, the cormorant booty had become a part of the energy of the gullery, digested in the stomachs of Argen's two nestlings.

The voracious sea hunt continued without pause, and together Argen and his mate pursued it. She had aroused his instinct to puddle and he had taught her much about the herring runs. In their fourth year together, the twelfth year of his life, the two birds began plundering the ternery island fairly regularly. Previously, when Argen had reconnoitered the island, his approach had been too direct and menacing and terns had filled the air to repel him. On one occasion he had been severely beaten, a score of the angry birds at his head, jabbing and ripping away at his eyes and head feathers.

Argen's two eggs had barely hatched when a raccoon invaded his territory one night, sent the gulls fleeing into the gloom, and ate the nestlings. In the days of indecision that followed, both birds awaited the resumption of the mating urge. They flew to the ternery together as they responded to the attraction of food there. Some young terns were out of their eggs, and the gulls, hovering offshore, could see balls of fluff hunched down on the sand. The female gull banked and landed among scattered rocks at a nestless tip of the island. Argen landed on a beach and began preening. He was filled with nervous expectation. The terns, except for odd screeching flights of inquiry overhead, did not molest them. Six swallows flew past, one so close to Argen's head that he heard its beak snap sharply over an insect.

The island became somnolent and tiny crabs scuttled in the shallows. Argen's mate began walking inland. He watched her doubtfully. He wanted to fly but was contained by his fear of an aerial attack by the terns. This inhibition eventually sent him on foot after her. Her erect form moved steadily forward, head darting from side to side as she picked up insects and scraps of food. Ahead, he could see the white forms of nesting terns and the flickering, sharp-pointed movements of flying birds. Argen was now surrounded by a white fire of water and the shadow of his head was at his feet. The heat bounded from the hot bare ground, and he breathed through open beak. The female stopped. Suddenly she darted forward and her head was obscured by a flailing wing. Argen saw an egg on the sand and ate it quickly. Now eggs and chicks were all around him and terns were rising like blown spume.

As the two gulls plundered, the terns flew very high and called plaintively. Argen and his mate became sated. They so dominated the ternery that they stood there in the sun, preening and cleaning their beaks, while the terns hovered and formed into screeching groups to circle the island. But they did not, unaccountably could not, attack the gulls.

From then on, till all the young terns were fledged and the ternery was beginning to break up, Argen and his mate plundered there individually and together. They could penetrate the terns' defenses on some days, but not on others. If they were accosted when approaching the island, they wheeled away. But if they were allowed to land, they were assured of a feast.

The two gulls flew to the mainland together and were caressed by a cool and soothing autumn, the estuary bubbling with shrimp and the air tumultuous with migrants. Argen's mate disappeared abruptly; for the first time in the four years of their association, he felt disturbed at this. He called out for her. But the feeling soon passed. He flew across the estuary in rain so heavy the water was alive with its fall.

The winter was to be a hard one. After a two-day blizzard, Argen drifted above blinding expanses of white dunes, white tidelands, white islands, white beaches, and then soared over a transformed estuary. From shore to shore and as far as he could see inland, the estuary was slowly and majestically on the move. It glided in a broken white mass under him and he saw the marbled green of patches of water between the ice floes and the cloudy whiteness of submerged ice. The sight of ice in the estuary excited him. When he had hunted and eaten, he soared over the estuary in the evening as the eastern sky became shot with red. The ice became metallic blue and moved irresistibly out to sea.

The river's ice, the incoming tides, ice floes from the ocean, inshore winds and biting cold, eventually jammed the estuary solidly. Chunks of ice ground against the islands in the estuary and, at the big island, undercut long sections of cliff and brought down massive falls of red soil. Many gulls died. The group with which Argen slept shrank from two thousand birds to fewer than two hundred as birds died or migrated. The winter scattered the gulls from the estuary and some arctic creatures occupied it. Snowy owls prowled the estuary in daylight and terrorized the gulls at night. Two of them eventually broke up Argen's group after attacking for three consecutive nights, killing one or two birds each night. Argen became so nervous as he strained to hear the owls' calls that he often flew suddenly and blindly in the dark. He would find himself aloft in thick snow when every movement was fraught with danger. He blundered into trees and under-growth and once even crashed into a sand dune, tumbling over and over on ice-encrusted sand. Eventually he gave up flight and stood still, trembling, not knowing where he was till the moon appeared or dawn dusted his surroundings with substance.

The winter abraded the spirit of all living things. Raccoons sleeping on the gullery island were wakened by the cold and went out into the snow and died. Swarms of snow buntings, refugees from the arctic, floated along the fringes of the estuary. When they settled, they drilled myriads of holes in the snow in search of summer grass seeds. Argen sometimes found numbed birds resting in the snow and ate them.

The estuary froze over eventually and ice began to build up along the shore as floes were driven in from the deep sea. Argen flew from one pool of black water to another in the estuary where uprisings of springs or chance currents had kept the ice clear. But he found little to eat. Offshore, a mosaic of floes stretched to the horizon. He went for days without food, and in his sleep he dreamed of the spring and the gullery.

Long before the spring came, Argen found himself stand-ing on high pieces of ground, on island cliffs, in treetops, on high sand dunes, facing eastward into the icy wind. From the sea would come the first of the gannets, terns, puffins, and murres. Their appearance, in his simple reckoning, would signify the imminence of the familiarity and excitement of the summer gullery.

He looked searchingly all through the closing days of winter while dazed seabirds came singly out of the sea and were wrecked in the ice on the shore, their will to live broken. Argen watched while hundreds of dispirited dovekies huddled together in offshore flocks. Some of them died at sea and were washed ashore, and their plight was Argen's good fortune. He looked into rustling walls of wet snow, the first sign of spring, and eventually found himself swathed in mist. The call of a seabird echoed and finally gave him the answer to the inexpressible question. He swept into the air crying and pumped down the estuary, screaming, screaming, screaming. That night, the estuary crackled and crashed with the sound of ice breaking up, and the winter was ended.

In the sea hunt was concealed the essence of a creature's spirit. Every creature was involved in different degrees. Some gulls were always victims of it, always harried, always extended, always uncomfortable. A few, like Argen, were stoically unvanquished by its worst moments and were able, even after such an evil winter, to emerge with renewed strength and authority.

In the spring he recognized his mate at once, though he had forgotten her during the latter part of the winter. He cried out his recognition, and she responded, and it was as though there had been no winter. Then came the familiar routines of life, the offshore flights, the puddling, the diving for urchins, the great towering flights in skies swept by a world of wind. Argen looked eagerly at the horizon. He was expectant and excited and he looked for new experience.

In twelve years he had never plundered the gannetry. The big birds were immune to the trickery he used with the cormorants. They stood fast on their nests against all intruders. The gannets were more than twice Argen's size, and he remembered seeing, one moonlit night years before, a raccoon cautiously snuffling up to a lone gannet nesting at the edge of the cliffs. The big bird had gargled her concern, stood up in the nest, and, as the raccoon hesitated, attacked and sent the animal rolling with a series of violent strokes of her beak.

As his mate incubated, Argen waited for hours on prominent rocks at the edge of the cliffs, watching the gannets passing back and forth from gannetry to ocean. He never saw an egg or a nestling left unguarded for a moment.

But no system of protection was invulnerable. He was watching the colony shortly before dusk settled one night, standing at the edge of the cliffs and already beginning to feel the pull that would eventually take him back to the nesting site, where he would sleep near his incubating mate. Now he was in the company of another gull, a stranger, who waited with him out of curiosity because he had identified Argen's presence at the cliffs with the hunt for food.

A distant commotion of gannets caught Argen's attention. The source of the sound was hidden from sight beyond a headland. Suddenly, wild panic gripped all the gannets. Argen held his ground even after he saw an eagle slowly beating along the cliffs. Gannets everywhere hurled themselves out to sea, each stomping down the sloping ground and sending eggs and nestlings and partially fledged birds scattering in great confusion. The fleeing birds stumbled over one another, knocked one another down, literally fell off the cliffs in struggling clots of motion before splintering and becoming airborne. Instantly, the sky moved with their bodies, and their trumpeting voices, *gaggla-gaggla-gaggla-gaggla*, roared back from the cliffs.

The eagle, disturbed at the gannets' reaction, directed his flight away from the island and at the same time dropped lower and passed well beneath the gannets. Argen, momentarily transfixed, had forgotten the gannetry. Then he looked back and saw eggs gleaming in the evening light, nestlings lurching and struggling to regain their feet, eggs broken, yolk running, splintered shell everywhere. He flew quickly down, gobbled at pools of yolk, and was swallowing a small nestling when angry gannets planed down and knocked him sprawling. He cried out, *ka-ka-ka*. But he was not fearful. He was victorious. Yolk dripped from his beak. He had tasted gannet flesh.

From then on, Argen watched for eagles. He followed in their wake, a cautious and retiring figure, flying low, ready to capitalize instantly on any confusion caused by the flight of the big birds. The sea hunt yielded to intelligence.

CHAPTER 16

In the Fall

ARGEN'S youngsters passed into the life of the shore and disappeared from his sight and care. But his mate remained constant to him, and his attachment for her survived through his thirteenth, fourteenth, and fifteenth breeding seasons. They put nine young gulls on the wing.

The most memorable time of the year for Argen was the fall, when the nestlings were independent and he and his mate were still together. The graying days stretched through a succession of comradely hunting expeditions. The two birds swept out over roaring surflines and, feathers disheveled, plunged into the roiling water, uncaring whether or not they caught prey, existing only for the moment.

They mounted the sky together and, in the company of scattered gulls, weaved and curved in wide arcs across the sky in exuberant expression of their contentment with the season. Sometimes they stayed aloft so long that the estuary darkened under them, became a silver tongue pointed at the dark sea, and they were still lit by the red glow of the setting sun.

But then, as the fall matured, their comradeship began slipping away. Argen was a resident of the estuary. His mate was not. She had been born half a continent away and was impelled to return to the south each winter. Argen watched her floating silently in the calm water, her reflection white as a cloud. He flew aimlessly along the red cliffs of the estuary island, long since empty of swallows. But in the moments before her departure, he drifted aimlessly in and out of the estuary. One day his mate was gone.

The fall was a time of withdrawal and the death of the breeding spirit of the summer. But it was also a time of intense activity for Argen. He had made the fall his special time. He hastened from place to place, preying on all the other creatures who, unlike himself, did not stand fast but fled at the slightest breath of cold.

By his thirteenth year Argen's fall behavior had developed a pattern. It began in the late summer, soon after he arrived from the gullery island. Small flocks of sandpipers from the arctic were gathering in the estuary, which they used as a collecting point before setting off for the south in mid-fall. They arrived by the hundreds, thousands, scores of thousands. Nearly every evening Argen paced their massed, rushing flights along the estuary shores as they flew to night roosting places. He would see flock upon flock swerve and undulate and suddenly fold, disappearing instantly, into a mass of their comrades who silently blotted out a wide-curving beach. It was here that Argen preyed. Almost every morning, infirm and dead sandpipers, the inevitable casualties of a mass migration, were easily scavenged. In the gray-shadowed pre-dawn light, Argen prowled silently along the beach, picking up sodden bodies bobbing in shallow water, hunting down stuporous sandpipers who fluttered to hopeless refuge in long grasses beyond the beach.

On almost the same day every year, Argen flew high over the estuary and headed out to sea again. He flew southeast, passing over part of the dunes, the ocean beach, seeing shoals of sand bowing gracefully in green water. He always flew alone. Nothing diverted him, not even the screaming gulls gathered in the estuary or the knots of gulls scavenging on stranded carrion along the ocean beach. He flew till the mainland diminished to a thread of blue and he came to a cluster of offshore islands.

The islands sat unexpectedly alone in the sea, host to a small colony of gulls and some terns and eider ducks. But Argen's interest in the islands was a shallow channel that cut between the two largest pieces of land. He floated over this channel in anticipation of the future and looked at the distinct pattern of the rocky, weed-strewn bottom, patched black, green, and gray in the shallow water. After gliding leisurely in the sea wind, he turned and landed on the peak of an old spruce, ruffled his feathers vigorously, and settled to wait.

Sometimes the herring came at night, most often soon after dawn, and rose to ripple the surface in such numbers that Argen was wakened or alerted. He yawned, stretched, and set out eagerly. The herring came toward the islands and were channeled, funneled, compressed in both width and depth, and so made the sea alive from shingle bottom to surface with their great numbers.

Argen, with a few hundred other excited gulls, floated, glided, paddled, dived, and screamed over the passage of the herring, knowing that this first great rush of fish would quickly taper off and that now was the time to gorge, gulp fish upon fish, till flying was impossible. The herring darkened the channel from bank to bank, and the sea appeared to move within itself, flowing southeast. Long before the herring thinned out, Argen had swum ashore and was swallowing uncomfortably in an effort to keep down his load of food.

Argen knew that the run would persist in a thinning straggle for five days and then abruptly end. He could anticipate the end of the run so precisely that, wakening on the island one morning, he returned to the mainland without even flying once more over the channel.

The fall brought multitudes of creatures to the estuary and many of them were Argen's prey. On dark, gusty nights, he listened half-attentively for sounds of distress in the air. The estuary was a great collecting place for migrating landbirds, particularly warblers. Argen waited for his chance to prey on the migrants.

It came one windy night, the moon blazing at the edge of an impenetrable cloud, doused, then blazing again, the estuary spectral in the changing light. Tisping, tweeting, piping calls came down twisting columns of air and Argen knew that the distress had begun. The night-flying landbird migrants, stimulated by the cold air, were heading confidently south when, unexpectedly, they collided with warm air moving in the opposite direction. Thousands of birds turned back and struck the cold air again, and the whole line of collision between warm and cold air became a conglomeration of birds, milling about.

From then on, Argen dozed intermittently as he waited for either the morning or some moonlight to permit night hunting. He took off before dawn and knew exactly where to hunt. The warblers were totally confused. They settled everywhere, on open ground, on beaches and mudflats, along rocky shorelines, in the dunes. Argen half flew, half ran among them and filled his crop with a score of birds before the sun rose. He preyed on the warblers till they regained their composure, usually by the following morning. Soon after, with a new wave of cold in the estuary, they were gone for the year.

There was another time, in early fall, that brought Argen to the estuary tidal flats. The summer crop of small fish was moving into the more sheltered waters of the estuary. They came in with the swelling tide, some of them even contained in the foam spilling across sandbars and in the scummy water advancing across mudflats.

As the small fry came inshore, flocks of terns dallied at the estuary for the hunting. Argen hunched on a sandbank and the terns rose thick as thistledown and began a jagged hunting dance. *Zip-zip-zip*, went their bodies, slicing like flat stones into the water. *Zip. Zip. Zip. Zip-zip. Zip-zip-zip.* Argen cocked a sleepy eye at the water as he sensed the increasing tempo of diving.

Then bigger fish, feeling the security of deeper water around them, began moving after the small fish, and at once Argen was in the air with other gulls, eyes searching the water for the sign of an unwary herring who, once seen, might attract a score of gulls dropping in pursuit. Further inshore, *zip-zip-zip* went the terns, weaving gracefully back and forth, up and down, in endless search for their tiny prey.

Argen's bounty of food in the fall was so great that he was transformed into a leisurely wanderer, free to observe the events of the season. Herons flew along the pebbly beaches of offshore islands and disappeared into stunted spruce along the mainland strand. Pairs of plovers ran at the edge of the sea as it foamed among the stones. Argen flew past ponds which were so still they seemed asleep, nestled behind high banks of stones thrust up by the surf. The banks protected the hinterlands of the islands and gave shelter to black ducks and eiders and many others, who skulked on cloud-stained water.

He saw rails standing in the shallows and hummingbirds hurtling madly in the troughs of waves, speeding from one fading island flower to another. Sparrows teemed in the thick vegetation at the shoreline and the skies above the estuary moved with brant geese banking down to feed on the eelgrass pastures. Argen flew offshore and was nearly cut down by a roaring flock of puffins moving out to sea. He turned high into the wind and, in the distance, saw arctic terns fleeting lightly over white-capped waves. Beyond them, a fast-moving cluster of phalaropes headed for the lee of an island to spend the night.

When the first touch of real cold came, Argen hastened to another fall meeting with his prey. All during the earlier part of the fall, when passing over the estuary marsh, he had seen scattered sora rails, most of whom had skulked almost unseen in the marsh during the summer but now were bursting into view in short, weak flights. Their plaintive wheeping calls intensified and Argen saw one rail flying unsteadily across a wide patch of water. He swerved to head it off. The rail, her short, chunky, almost tail-less body tense with awareness of his intentions, made a desperate effort to reach safety among some reeds. But Argen struck her down in mid-air and dropped to the water to feed on her crippled body.

The estuary dissolved into rains and blinding mists driven in from the offshore banks. In the worst of this turbulent weather, Argen eagerly awaited the next episode in his fall hunting. In the midst of a storm, ducks began arriving at the estuary. Argen heard them shortly before dawn, invisible to

him, only distinguishable by their quacks and gabbles overhead. In the gray birth of morning, he flew slowly along the
estuary shores, now crackling with new ice. Scattered flocks
of black ducks were there, moving down the coast in
search of winter hunting grounds. The next day, a flock of
eiders filled an inlet while thick mist rolled over their heads.

Over the years, the ducks came to the estuary in vast
numbers. They came by sea and by land, in calm weather
and, in particular, in storms. They seemed unaffected by
weather and could fly in gales that grounded all other birds.
There seemed to be no order in their movements, but there
was distinct order in Argen's predatory watch on them. He
knew now that any large gathering produced a certain number of crippled and sick birds. He watched and waited for
them, found ducks hiding in marsh-grass thickets, skulking in
shoreline vegetation, dead in the shallows. All during the late
fall and early winter, he fattened and grew sleek.

But it was the geese he remembered best in the fall. They
had a special place in his time sense because they were usually the first to herald spring, their northing, three-toned calls
coming out of black and snow-beset skies as they plunged
north. Their calls sent shivers through Argen's skin as he
recognized the undefeated voice of life, stronger than ice,
more powerful than the hurricane.

When the geese came south again, he watched them, his
attention caught by the power and size of their bodies. He
rarely preyed on them, for few were stricken during their
migration. After a preliminary V-flight over the estuary, the
geese came swinging over the island spruces and suddenly
revealed the broadness of powerful wings beating back to
slow their approach. One hundred bodies hissed into the
water and the air snapped with braking wings. Argen hov-

ered, watching. In turn, he was watched by a tall gander who, standing apart from the rest of the geese, acted as a sentinel. He warned Argen, with a throaty gabble, not to approach too closely.

When the real winter began, ducks and geese were still arriving. Some flocks, after circling the estuary, landed on shoreline ice and slipped and fell over themselves as they glissaded to a stop. They came in gales that ripped off the top of the sea and blew it inland, when spindrift came inshore fifty wingspans thick and Argen had to crouch merely to hold his roosting position on land. They passed the estuary in blizzards; Argen, from a sheltered position on the estuary island, saw them aloft, their wings invisible as they sought to make passage against the wind. He heard them quacking at night in gales, as they were carried on to destinations they had not chosen.

Finally, the migrating was done. Argen looked into the gray sea and felt the chill of its depths. The sun was gone and ahead was only the dread of spray freezing at midnight, the antic roar of gales sweeping ice-clotted sand into the sleeping flocks of gulls, the sibilance of wind among the dunes and the whisper of snow sailing in from the sea.

Argen's spirit did not waver. He stood squarely in the wind. His stomach was full and he was warm and serene. At such times, he was able to look forward and see himself, alive and thriving, in the next spring at the strand.

CHAPTER 17

A Sleep of Time

THE seasons folded into each other and Argen felt a touch of lassitude as, inert, replete, and sleepy, he allowed the tide to wash over his feet. Time was measured by periods between sleep, sometimes lengthy when life was active, sometimes short when there was little purpose except staying alive. He slept briefly in his youth, reluctantly in his dynamic middle years, and now, at sixteen, his joints stiffened slightly in moments of rest. He remained the great hunter, nervous about falcons and inexplicable noises and shadows, his strength and alertness undiminished. But sleep drew him back from the insistent realities of his life.

Sleep came to him in several forms. Mostly, he slept with his eyes half-closed or occasionally shut, with his head buried in his fluffy back feathers, one leg pulled up into the equally fluffy feathers of his abdomen. In this pose, he slept anywhere, perhaps waiting at the fringe of a full or depleted tide, perhaps passing the time of heavy rain or fog which made hunting impossible.

His sleep was less a response to exhaustion than it was an adjustment to tides and the availability of food, a reflection of mood. He dozed in mid-morning when the estuary was silently moving at the peak of a spring tide. He slept away a night of biting cold winds, when he relapsed into true sleep, so well fluffed out that he became a feathered sphere, only his leg and tail protruding into the cold.

But there was another dimension to sleep which had, over the years, become a formal part of his life. Sleeping and resting were vulnerable times and the herring gulls tended to congregate during these periods. As a juvenile, Argen instinctively joined such groups and so assuaged his fear of the unknown. As he grew older, this fear increased. Behind it lurked the memory of helpless terror in the marsh. He sought, and found, a place of absolute security, of absolute familiarity. This was the place of his deepest sleeps, where, in the company of thousands of other gulls with an identical urge, he could sleep securely.

Every evening in late summer, fall, and winter, he became part of a concourse of herring gulls drifting south over marsh and dune to the communal sleeping grounds. The evening flights in late summer were exciting. As far as Argen could see ahead of him, herring gulls, lit by the slanting golden light of the sun, pumped steadily along to their common destination. They traveled loosely, never more than a score in a group, frequently flying alone or in twos and threes. All were part of a great cyclical common experience. All saw the hollows in the dunes darkening beneath them and the rolling green dune plants turning purple, then black. All saw the ocean turning ocherous in the last moments of light. All saw the tide and sand glistening ahead of them in the last light of the sunken sun.

The sleeping grounds lay among shallow sand shoals and vestigial dunes beyond the southern limits of the ocean beach and south of the large complex of dunes and marshes that flanked the southern rim of the estuary. The area was riven by channels of water which discouraged land-bound predators. It was open, treeless, bushless, and grassless and no predator could approach without being seen.

To settle in this territory, Argen knew, was to sink deeply into the security of the known and the predictable. He dropped to a landing and watched latecoming birds, lit pink, orange, red, as they glided into land, and then, after dark, heard the latecomers hissing in to near-blind landings among their comrades.

Sleep here was a deeply sustaining experience. In the darkest nights of fall when the fogged sky pressed down on the gulls, Argen would scarcely stir when a bright whip of lightning lit the birds for a moment in a stark tableau. He would feel the red glow fading in his closed eyes and might open them for a moment when a heavy bump of thunder shook the ground.

In winter, when the congregated gulls were reduced to a small fraction of their late-summer and fall numbers, he sank into his deepest sleeps, drawing himself in against the penetrating chill which froze water on his feathers. He slept on one foot, but when it became chilled he dropped his warm foot and drew the cold member up against his belly. He rocked in winds, felt snow building up on his fluffed feathers, shook himself without fully waking. He slept through torrential spring rains which coursed so heavily in the sand at his feet that he sank into it and found himself walking, still half asleep, to firmer ground. These rains, which followed the worst of winter's cold, signified his imminent departure for the gullery, for less secure, more exciting nights when, many times, he would have no sleep at all.

When he awoke in the mornings, always long before any sign of dawn, the serried lines of his comrades were visible under starlight or moonlight. He watched them as he prepared for the new day, stretching, yawning, preening, and saw the faintest iridescence growing around them as pale light grew out of the air. He was the first away from the sleeping grounds, up and away into dusky quiet, and a thousand gulls saw the sweep of white wings, heard his soft *ka-ka* call, and so were roused to begin their day.

Sleep was an intermission between events, and Argen awoke from it, at any time of the year, with a feeling of restoration and eagerness to hasten on to the next event. He wakened from sleep at the gullery with the late sun rebounding from a flat and featureless sea and saw a host of gulls towering silently against a sharp horizon. He wakened with a start at his mate's cry as she, still far distant, told him she had hunted, her crop was full, the nestlings would be fed.

He dozed, standing on the bluffs of the estuary island, sleepy after the excitement of hunting at dusk and drenched in the glow of the dying day. He slept while the magnificence of the east swept across the horizon of the land, and the estuary water, rippled by the faintest movement of air and current, radiated the color of the sky. Thick banks of smoky blue clouds bunched along the horizon. He started awake and saw the black shapes of gulls silhouetted against the orange sky. The cool upper sky pressed the orange sunset slowly down out of sight.

Sleep was the antidote to fear and even to hunger. Sleep was such sweet withdrawal that, as he aged, passing insensibly out of his middle years, it was welcomed, luxuriously anticipated. He slept, oblivious. He slept on a solitary rock while beneath him a starfish crept slowly and blindly to a mussel and fastened its arms to the mussel's shell. The starfish pulled steadily throughout the morning while Argen slept. The tide turned, Argen awoke, the mussel was exhausted and gaped open; as Argen pumped across the sunwhite water, the starfish inserted its stomach into the mussel's shell and ate its body.

Argen slept on the tidelands, the water far distant, waiting, and under his feet whelks forced their snailish bodies through the sand in blind search for clams, against whose shells they abraded rows of teeth, scraped holes, and gained entry to the succulent flesh. Argen's sleep was a tiny serene void in the torrent of life. He slept while young salmon, shad, and smelt spilled through the estuary and into the sea. He slept while uncountable millions of fish retreated to the warmer south and while schools of young herring formed in readiness for the winter. He slept while the cod legions moved from the shore for the warmth of offshore deeps.

The estuary turned subtly blue, became metallic and calm at the touch of early fall, and concentrations of gulls and wading birds stood in the shallows. Argen slept intermittently while the bright lives of migrants glowed around him. He slept while a golden plover, the greatest migrant, dozed uneasily near him, balanced on one foot. As the wind changed direction almost imperceptibly, the plover swiveled his body with it. *Wheer-wheer*, cried a group of plovers, and swept down the sand tidelands. *Pit-pit-pit*, cried the sandpipers, and roared into the dusk. *Tow-lee*, cried the yellowlegs, and broke their own mirrored reflections in the water with long slender legs.

Argen rocked back and forth, feathers well fluffed, head

hunched down into his back, eyes half-lidded, and his lethargy cloaked a thick welling up of memories. The puffins and the murres burst out of the sea and passed across water smoking with spume and disappeared out of sight in his dream. The cormorants watched him tensely and the gannets led him to runs of fish far offshore. He dreamed he was hovering on moonlit wings and the petrels cut past him like nighthawks.

Argen's life touched many others with its ceaseless energy. His wings shadowed red beaches in a remembered dream and drove him, dancing in weird jerks, into groups of moths as he hawked them out of the night air like a flycatcher; he flew into masses of flying ants and beat them into clots of turbulence and his beak smacked among them. In the afterglow of a sunset, he glided past a legion of flying spiders and circled to pick them, drowned and drowning, out of the incoming tide. He was feeding on purple berries inland and then, in an abrupt change of memory, was flying smoothly into a gripping northeasterly which ballooned him up a thousand wingspans in a few seconds and from this giddy height he watched the estuary torn to foam.

He slept, the moonlight cool, the water bronzed, and dreamed of swordfish waiting, like himself, for the herring to run and heard the barking of seals in mist as they plunged down off glistening rocks into deep water, where, they knew, lobsters were shucking their shells. The lobsters knew they were vulnerable and hid. The whales knew where the thickest concentrations of plankton were in spring and fall, and the flounders knew where the herring spawned and ate their eggs. The knowledge of the strand was spread among all the creatures and it even animated the tissue of ocean-going jellyfish, which were nothing more than purplish gasbags supporting trailing poisonous tentacles. Argen often saw them, driving inshore in an easterly wind, brainless, heartless, lungless, limbless, but their gasbags were all trimmed to delay, as long as possible, their fatal meeting with the shore.

Argen flew slowly and deliberately along the lee shore of islands, sheltered from the growingly keen winds, and saw ducks gathering along the shore, ducks trailing ducklings through the waves, ducks gathering in all-female flocks, ducks hastening down rocky foreshores followed by lines of ducklings. He flew along the island shores at sunset and saw the water cut by a blinding track of light; the suns of a hundred evenings sank into the west.

He awoke, aroused by his acute sense of time, and rose into the air. He carried lightly his knowledge of where the mussels lived, and how to dive for urchins, the best time to hunt clams, where to puddle for worms, how to break a snail shell, how to cheat others out of their food, when to fly offshore to feed, how to protect his family against raccoon attacks, how to pillage the ternery, and when to look for exhausted migrants, where to find storm victims, when the seals were hunting and how dangerous they were. Best of all, at this time of the year, he knew the tidal overturn in the estuary with its great late-season proliferation of living things and he flew eagerly. He knew the shape and force of weather yet to come, even though he hunted in the midst of almost constant turbulence where two opposing forces, the dryness of the land and the dampness of the sea, were forever engaging and disengaging and shaping the climate.

As he now flew toward the thickest clustering of birds in the estuary, the air went suddenly dark. The encircling dark-green hills became blue, then magenta. The sun was blotted out by rolling gray vapor. Vivid lines of electricity crackled out of the upper darkness and thunder rumbled across the estuary and rippled down the coast. Mingled with this were the screams of the birds, eerie now, diminished into insignificance by the power around them. Argen headed into the murk. Other birds around him plunged along in search of shelter.

Then came torrential rain. The estuary disappeared. Birds blundered into one another. Argen turned from a burning flash of lightning. His nerves tingled. He struck a cormorant in mid-air, gasped, plunged away to the surface, and passed over a score of terns huddled on a floating branch.

As Argen flew, the rain stopped as suddenly as it had begun, as though cut off in mid-air. It left behind a gasping vacuum. The estuary appeared, rematerialized, rather, out of fleeing vapor, and revealed a wild mixture of birds at every level of flight, on the water, milling and screaming.

The hills were blue again. The seaward side of the estuary suddenly glowed with sunlight. It did not appear from any single point, but radiated with such heat that the adjacent hills dissolved into white fire. Then the source, the sun, broke through a circular hole in the overcast. A shaft of light joined the sky to the estuary and signified the end of the thunderstorm and the beginning of evening.

Argen headed across the estuary he knew so well.

CHAPTER · 18

The Long Scavenge

AT SIXTEEN Argen was the oldest gull at both the estuary and the gullery. He revealed his age by his slower movements, his long sleeps among the communal gatherings of gulls at the estuary and along ocean beaches. His imperfect right wing now became slightly frayed at the tip from hitting water and land when he took off. But when he was active, it was clear that age had not touched his restless, aggressive spirit. During dark nights at the change of season, he would take off silently from among his sleeping comrades and go winging off across the sea alone. The other gulls stirred restlessly at his departure but lacked the stimulus to trigger them into flight. Then, far in the distance, Argen's triumphant food cries sounded and the other gulls rose in a hiss of wings. They knew that with Argen as the beacon they would find good hunting.

But Argen's confidence and supremacy concealed an inner distress. All during his sixteenth summer, luminously bright with keen winds and moonlit nights trembling on the water, he sensed a change on the horizon of his life. He could not see or hear it; he felt it through the subtlest of his senses.

(203)

He stood on the eastern cliffs, facing into a hot wind, his breeding finished, his mate flying overhead, and he began screaming. *Koy-koy-koy*, and the sea moved toward him. *Koy-koy-koy-koy-koy*, he screamed, and his body twisted as he struggled to expel every drop of emotion. Other gulls joined him as they reacted to the expression of their own forebodings. Argen, now walking up and down as he screamed, was soon the center of a group of agitated birds. But the sea rolled on silently and revealed nothing.

In the late summer and early fall, Argen felt the first impact of the change in the sea. When he flew to the offshore banks, the anticipated uprisings of young fish and plankton were not there. Kittiwakes flew rapidly in compact flocks, buzzing inquiring calls as they sought the feeding grounds. But the ocean was silent and empty. The uprisings, now located several days' flying to the south, would eventually draw all the oceanic birds to them. The great northern current, resurgent because of weather changes in the arctic, had collided with the southern current and had warped it away from the coast in a wide curve to the south.

Argen floated high and watched. Soon he saw a sign. The bodies of hundreds of small fish, each less than half the length of his wing, appeared under him. He landed quickly and ripped and tore at the nearest dead fish, a menhaden. But as the days passed, he and all the other gulls and seabirds became sated. The fish came up steadily from the depths. Currents and winds moved their bodies into sweeping patterns across the ocean. Argen, floating high, saw them disappearing into the distance. In places, the surface was roiled by the glistening rounded backs of porpoises and whales moving steadily though the floating menhaden.

As Argen floated, crop bulging, eyes dulled with eating, the menhaden were still struggling underwater to resolve the disaster that had engulfed them. As the cold water spread over the offshore shallows, it had caught many fish sheltering in submarine canyons and valleys. The cold water poured over the peaks on both sides of the valleys and trapped the warmer water beneath it. This overbearing mass of cold water confronted the countless fish in the valleys with a crisis. Nearly all of them were highly sensitive to even the slightest change in water temperature. The cod and haddock, which could withstand quite severe cold, drove up through the cold layer and escaped. Some of the menhaden and many herring found warm fissures in the cold and fled along them. But most of the menhaden waited helplessly while the cold water bore down and squeezed the warmth out of the valleys, and were eventually surrounded. Some, in panicky rushes into the cold, escaped to warmer water, but most died in their flight.

The changes in the ocean had widespread effects on the movement of air and of climate generally. They would determine the nature of the coming winter. Argen faced into a new sea wind and sensed unseasonable chill as a wave of arctic air rolled down the strand. That night, his feet stuck to clots of freezing sand and above him he heard the cries of disturbed migrants who were attempting to outfly the cold. The wind from the north bit into Argen's neck. By morning, a crystalline day, the estuary was gripped in a thin sheath of ice. Argen flew in silent observation along the whites and grays of a season that was not due, according to his time sense, for another sixty days.

The effect of the premature freeze on the rest of life was explosive. The gulls scattered like thistledown and hastened south and west. Argen listened to the uproar of movement in the night air as migrant birds, trapped by the unexpected cold as the menhaden had been in the sea, sought to burst through to the warmth of the south. The migrants rested and died at the estuary. Numbed warblers sheltered among rocks along the shores and Argen hunted them all day. Butterflies, chilled into immobility, dropped from upriver trees and swirled in the estuary currents. It was a season of revolution. Ducks piled into estuary inlets and scattered bright chips of ice as they broke through the skin that had formed on the water.

Argen flew along the shoreline. Here and there a heron or a rail sprawled in an odd posture, gripped by wing and claw in the ice. A score of juvenile herring gulls clustered, dead and icily rigid, by a frozen lagoon. Robins, drawn suddenly together by the cold, hastened across the estuary. The high upper air moved with hawks and crows migrating together, oblivious of each other's presence.

Argen watched and was profoundly disturbed. In the ensuing days, which were tumultuous with a foreign mixture of ice and rain, gales and paralyzing freezes, the gulls disappeared quickly from the estuary. Argen saw his mate crossing the estuary in a shroud of torrential rain and he did not see her again. Within a score of days, fewer than a thousand gulls remained of the ten thousand who frequented Argen's sleeping grounds. This number soon sank to fewer than one hundred. The sand and mudflats of the sleeping grounds lay hard and bright as iron and Argen felt a chill other than from cold.

The winter lay so heavily that it stifled the estuary. The water was gripped solid, no black pools, no passing ducks; Argen was driven to the ocean shore, where he prowled uneasily among a solid jam of ice floes. Soon the estuary population of gulls leveled off at a few score of older birds who, like Argen, were held by tradition to the place they knew best. They slept closely together while, in the worst cold, thick snow shrouded them; the wind brought from the sea the grinding sound of ice rising and falling.

As the snow and ice thickened, the gulls found an unexpected source of food. Ice crushing against the shoreline pulverized mussels and scraped shellfish off rocks. The ice dragged the bottom, caught up oysters, and, in time, passed them up through its substance to the surface. Argen and his comrades prowled the ice jams and tugged at the shattered and frozen wreckage of the shellfish.

The abrasive winter depleted Argen; it killed some of the remaining gulls. The winter made him thin, ragged, and, for the first time, aged. The season drew its spirit directly from the arctic. Argen frequently became lost in blizzards which blotted out the estuary and all the shore for days at a time. Even on clear days the air was milky white. Argen paused on an ice hummock in the middle of the estuary. As usual, he was the only gull in sight. Absolute silence held the air still as stone. He looked beyond mountains of snowdrifts winding among uptilted ice pans.

But the winter did not dispirit him. He endured ice storms in which torrential rains, near freezing, drowned the shore, then froze solidly on landing. He slithered and stumbled over glittering sheets of ice that covered everything and hung in massive stalactites from cliffs. He slept uneasily to the thuds and crashes of falling limbs and trees all along the shore.

His spirit swelled with the spring. When his mate reappeared at the beginning of a hard, bright season, he was finished molting. The estuary became turbulent under high winds after its ice had ground and bobbed out to sea, and Argen rose into the thrust of the wind. His expectation of the flight to the gullery took him, screaming, high over the water, and a thousand birds rose willingly under him as his voice whipped toward them. The gull flocks had all suffered heavy losses during the winter, and the urge to breed seemed heightened.

As Argen flew to the gullery for the first time that season, he faced a new kind of wind. It was unseasonable, gustless, blowing with solid and exhausting power from the southeast. It brought neither rain nor mist, but after the gullery was occupied, it sent a mosaic of clouds passing rapidly overhead.

Argen rose from the gullery, swept through a thicket of dead spruces, and banked into the wind. Under him, gannets lifted their wings and were instantly airborne. He saw murres cautiously skirting the cliffs as they tested the sideways thrust of the wind, then turning toward the cliffs, beating rapidly as they strove to avoid being hurled against the rock. Some murres, in exposed positions, turned fully into the wind and backed themselves into their cliffside refuges with quick glances behind them, wings blurred and paddle feet kicking to maintain equilibrium.

Argen rose steeply till he found himself caught up in the turbulent upthrust of wind from the cliffs. He tried to glide but was torn one way and another, pushed up, pulled down abruptly, till he became impatient and, reversing the plane of his wings, swooped down at blinding speed, using the wind's force to drive him, like a wedge, under it. He curved past dancing flocks of kittiwakes and then soared up again and the speed of his climb dizzied him.

The endless wind had a cumulative effect on the ocean. It gradually moved the upper layer of water toward the shore. There, building up pressure, the water layer turned under itself and drifted along the bottom. As Argen and his mate ranged to the offshore banks, the underwater current became a stream, flushing the inshore area clear of much of its normally dense planktonic life. Diatoms, flagellates, copepods, herring larvae, and young cod were driven inshore at the surface, carried offshore underwater.

Argen, battling the wind, found the hunting unrewarding. He ranged widely as he sought the now elusive herring. Traces of them rippled tantalizingly in the track of the sun, but none of Argen's great knowledge of their movements was useful this year. He could never know the confusion of the herring as they met the cold northern current, the streaming submarine flow, the strange mixture of temperatures. The herring schools tried repeatedly to get inshore to the shallows. But the cold and the currents always stood in their way.

Argen turned against the wind and felt its force tilt and sweep him toward the invisible mainland. Beneath him, well out of sight in deep water, a horde of herring were moving offshore in a current that sprang away from the mainland. Soon, far offshore, they would spawn.

Spring's hard cold days of winds blowing out of achingly white skies persisted into summer and Argen cried out from a dead spruce. His mate rose from near her nest, still empty because the food shortage had delayed the breeding cycle. Both birds were ravenous. They flew along the eastern cliffs, searching. Above them, gannets, also hungry, swept away on great food-hunting journeys several days' flight out to sea. But hunting was meager everywhere. Argen listened vainly for food cries. He watched gannets, cormorants, puffins, and murres in expectation of their finding food. But the sea heaved in hollow curves and the shore was barren. Argen and his mate returned to the gullery with empty crops.

The downturn of populations of fish was affecting most of

the creatures along the shoreline. Without herring, there was no inshore migration of cod. Without herring, predatory squid were ravenous. Argen, struggling down into shallow water in an effort to reach some shellfish, saw a squid attacking a small school of herring. The squid, jet-propelled, bit the herring into debris, some of which floated up to Argen, and he choked and gobbled at each scrap of flesh as the squid lanced back and forth under his kicking legs.

When his mate hatched two eggs, the quest for food became critical. In response, Argen began harrying gulls he suspected of having food in their crops and sometimes, by the ferocity of his attacks, made them disgorge. He stood on the gannet cliffs and watched hunters returning from the sea. When he saw puffins carrying small fish to their burrows, he chivied them relentlessly; sometimes they dropped the fish. He drove gulls off their nests and pillaged eggs and nestlings. He and his mate now attacked the ternery almost every day. Argen found he could fly directly into the ternery at any time without being struck by the defensive terns.

The terns had thus far survived the famine by making progressively longer hunting trips; but Argen's attacks, often in concert with other hungry gulls who followed his lead, brought the terns to the end of their resistance. One morning, Argen landed on the island in a buffeting wind and walked under the customary canopy of screeching birds. Suddenly the terns' cries changed in quality and became plaintive, lost, haunted with inexpressible feeling. Birds rose from the ground all round Argen and whisked away like snowflakes. Thousands of them twisted into flight. The ternery dwindled as the birds struggled to be free of it. Many of them gathered high above the island and finally broke the bond that held them. They fled, in an emotional concourse, away across the sea. Argen was left alone. He looked at the odd terns still circling offshore as though unable to resolve their bafflement. He looked at eggs in the sun and at nestlings crouched against the sand waiting for parents who had gone forever. The terns, in memory of that moment of dread, would not reoccupy the island for years. The ternery was cleaned out by gulls. Patches of broken eggshells were the only signs that a great host had lived there.

Argen sustained his youngsters by robbery and scavenging; but as the days passed he sensed that the gullery was breaking up. The destruction of the ternery was but a brief respite; thousands of gulls drifted away to the mainland and left eggs and sometimes dead or dying youngsters. The shallows along the western side of the island became a gathering place for flocks of idle, waiting gulls. Their purpose at the island was unfulfilled.

Argen and his mate stood together and their chicks at their breasts were constantly noisy with hunger. Gangs of juvenile gulls roamed through the gullery and intimidated birds already disturbed by the famine. Argen watched them gathering at points across the gullery and harassing adult gulls trying to defend their nests. When the hungry young gulls approached his territory, he reacted with shrill cries and menacing rushes which drove them away. As soon as his own youngsters were on the wing, he and his mate left the island and flew to the estuary. His youngsters, thin but healthy, soon followed them in a small group of first-year birds; later they migrated south, in search not of warmth but of food.

The hunger persisted. Argen was constantly alert for carrion. When stalking the ocean beach, he found a number of old carcasses of cod, mackerel, and haddock, fish that had died or been killed at sea and had missed being eaten. Their bodies were so desiccated that no amount of tugging would dislodge much flesh. He pulled at the dry body of an old pollock one day and then found himself dragging it down toward the water, as though he were about to wash it. Once he had the pollock in the shallows, he felt more sure of his actions and redoubled his efforts to rip flesh from it. Then, as the carcass soaked up water, it became soft and pieces of it came away. Eventually Argen ate all of the dehydrated fish and left nothing but a skeleton in the shallows.

He and his mate found themselves alone in a disintegrating season. When the first splotches of snow touched their feathers as they dozed at the sleeping grounds south of the estuary, the female roused herself, yawned, and rose into the air. Argen watched. She was flying indecisively. She turned back and forth low across the smooth milky water, then disappeared into the snow haze; but almost immediately she returned and landed near Argen. She was looking at him. She could not understand why her desire to migrate was not impelling her south. She landed and immediately fluffed out her feathers and dozed. A sickness in her was overmastering her drive to go south.

While his mate sank into lethargy, Argen went on with his routines of fall and their relationship of the summer ended. She floated listlessly in bays and inlets while he, far distant, dived for the few shellfish survivors of the previous winter's ice pack. He flew to the herring-run islands, but this merely brought him five days of hungry waiting in a thin gray rain. On his return, he wandered over marsh and dune, meagerly scavenging crusted flesh in old shells. The ocean beach yielded only scraps of life in piles of weeds.

The slender days grew thinner and Argen's gut tightened. He looked at the new ice and remembered the pain of winter and from his hunched stance looked across the estuary. He felt changed and vaguely disturbed. There was little anger to send him blazing away in pursuit of life. He felt drained. He looked dully at other gulls drifting across the leaden water, and the sky filled with black clouds and snow drifted across his eyes.

In the midst of his lethargy, he became aware of his mate's presence at the estuary. He recognized her first by her voice, which sounded in high agitation from a nearby sandbar. He responded by flying over the sandbar and crying out. Throughout the hungry days, her cries were so insistent, so passionate, so expressive of her bafflement at the famine, that they aroused Argen's memory and he flew after her as she swept down the estuary. The two birds fell into a similar routine of hunting and found themselves scavenging together at sea and in the estuary. Argen's lethargy gradually disappeared as he followed in the wake of a familiar fantail and heard cries that evoked easier and less troublesome times at the strand.

Eventually he hunted as though some of the female's spirit had been transferred to him and he beat into rustling sheets of snow in search of her. He joined her on a sandbar, where she was pulling at the disintegrating body of a waterlogged hare. He landed and faced into a white wind and screamed his spirit, *Koy-koy-koy-koy.* His mate echoed him, *Kee-kee-kee-kee.* The two birds swung out over the snow-muffled sea and beat steadily through the white silence.

The famine united them and it forced them to travel in search of food. They roamed far down the coast and passed into a new territory where another river system and estuary debouched into the sea. They flew up the river and were in a deep river valley together, dark water reflecting dark trees, and a white sky hovered just above their heads.

The valley was mottled white and green, and after sleeping in a spruce tree the two birds flew as a roseate dawn washed the new sun and the river with color. But the hunting was meager. Argen led the way up a subsidiary river, almost a stream, where, in the shallows, they found and trapped several young fish and ate them before forcing on up into the dark hills.

The stream wound on between narrowing banks, and eventually the two gulls were heading north again, driving into belts of wet snow as the stream petered out and they passed over a range of hills and glided down into another valley. Argen was oppressed by the expanses of forest which stretched in rolling waves into snow haze. He looked in vain for the comforting division between land and water where, he knew, there should be a sufficiency of food. *Ka-ka*, he called to his mate, and she responded and they flew on into the murk, aching with hunger.

The days in the hills were rigorous, and gusty winds blew the gulls roughly over the lashing tops of evergreens. They settled at the edges of black streams and whirlwinds of snow enveloped them. Argen, seeing hares in the deepening snow, prowled open ground in the forest and caught a youngster, which he killed after a spirited struggle. The gulls reached another river one morning. They both unhesitatingly turned downstream. An urgent desire to return to the sea was in both of them.

The river was their pathway to the estuary and their flight was narrowly contained between sloping, tree-covered banks. Here and there, waterfalls plunged noisily into the river. The gulls flew silently and at times saw their white reflections fleeing across water smooth as moonlight.

They flew and rested and ate only red berries, found at the edge of the river. Gradually the river widened and shallowed, and odd islands split its slowing current. Argen saw an owl beating hurriedly from one island to another. The water speckled with life and the gulls settled to feed on an uprising of minnows. Argen was so hungry that he gobbled blindly and swallowed more water than he did fish. He was conscious only of the distension of his crop and the wriggling inside it.

For a while the familiarity of the estuary comforted the two gulls. Argen felt his dreads dwindle when, in the middle of a freezing night, he awoke and saw his mate outlined in the moonlight, her body trembling with her breathing. But hunting was still difficult and Argen became accustomed to the female bird's crying and indecisive flying. She disappeared one afternoon and did not return till the middle of the following day. The two birds settled on an ice floe and drifted slowly across dark-blue water.

Argen now sensed the female's distress. At last she was dominated by her hunger. She left the estuary the next day and flew steadily down the ocean beach to the south. Argen followed at a distance, not wanting to leave a sure source of food, however meager, in the estuary. When he overtook the female, standing high on the beach, with all her feathers fluffed out she looked twice her normal size. He settled, cautiously expectant and waited to see if she had found food, but when dusk came and she had not yet moved, he returned alone to the estuary. The night was a moaning of black winds. At dawn Argen flew again along the ocean beach, not in search of the female but drawn by the possibility that she had found food. He saw her. She had changed neither her position nor her stance. He hovered and called, but she did not react. Her eyes were closed and her body trembled with her breathing. Argen was puzzled by the unresponsive, unmoving gull and he settled on the top of a dune.

After a gray and freezing midday, with a suggestion of

snow in the air, the female gull fell on her side and tremors shook her wings. Gradually her neck arched back; her eyes were still closed and her legs and wings stretched straight behind her till at last the tremors stopped and she was still.

Argen had risen to his feet and now he walked along the dune softly crying *kuk-kuk-kuk;* but he became impatient eventually and returned to the estuary to feed. The following day, when he flew down the ocean beach in an agitation of memory, he saw no trace of the dead gull. The sand had been swept clean by a high tide and clotted with black humps of dead weeds. Argen called to the unresponsive ocean.

The winter seeped into Argen's bones and made him dull-eyed with the effort of his resistance to it. All around him, herring gulls were dying; after a hard night of snow and wind, he saw the bodies of some of them working uneasily in the viscid shallows. He survived partly because he found a colony of muskrats in an inland marsh. They were stuporous with the cold and he dug them out of the ice-stiffened rubbish of their shelters and, after battering and smashing, broke up their bodies enough to swallow them. He only gave up hunting them when a mink, hungry as he, leaped out silently from a clump of frozen grasses, cold eyes fastened on his throat.

When spring came hauntingly out of the white vapors of the winter, it revealed a humbled strand. The swallows never returned to the red cliffs of the estuary; their empty burrows were like hollow staring eyes in the cliffs. The island of terns remained deserted; no terns appeared anywhere near the estuary or offshore. Migrants poured north, but few gulls returned to the estuary. Argen kept hearing echoes in this sustained emptiness of life remembered and of life expected. He beat upward through gray morning mists to meet an orange explosion of sunlight and looked across an undulating mass of mist; he saw he was alone. He looked for familiar sights, gull wings jerking, gulls wheeling in the wind, but did not find them.

Gradually, however, gulls trickled into the estuary. Argen was caught up in the force of life that they created and was pressed slowly into new service. By the time the gulls were ready to leave for the gullery, Argen was mated to a small female, a young bird but recently matured who did not yet have a powerful breeding urge. She importuned him for food and her cries were querulous; but she did not fly with him, or mate with him at the estuary, and their only meeting point was among the groups of resting gulls on a particular sandbar near the ocean beach.

This year, the assault on the gullery was filled with sinister undertones. No familiar hordes of gulls rose exultantly over the estuary. The flight to the gullery was a thin straggle of almost silent birds, suddenly lost in an expanse of sea spread before them. All was strange. The gullery was charged with unfamiliar shadows and the angular spruces glowed with white fire. Argen's outstretched feet approached earth a score of times, but each time he flew up in terror. The female did not share his concern. She floated high above him and was remote from the tension of the leader gulls who felt impelled to land on the island.

After three days, when the birds were safely settled on the island, they were so spread out, with so much territory to share among them, there was scarcely any fighting. Argen dominated the knoll. He looked out watchfully and eagerly into the emptiness and, disturbingly, into the quiet. But soon more gulls began arriving, and as the weather became warmer and the volume of gull calls grew, Argen felt slightly more at ease on the island.

But he was not well accustomed to his mate, though they copulated and she laid two eggs. She had a poor impulse to incubate. Argen's impulse was strong, and so he found himself left on the nest for long periods. After ten days, he became irritated and began standing up in the nest and calling out for her. She, far distant, was responding to her pubescent urge to search, and to know. She was not yet firmly gripped by a mature mating urge. She drifted up and down sea and shore in aimless and leisurely exploration. One day she simply did not return.

This left Argen in a ferment of indecision. He incubated throughout the night, but in the morning, after being forced off the nest by bursting bowels, he stood indecisively nearby and preened. Shortly after sunrise, the eggs now cold and dead, he resolved his unease by eating the eggs.

He remained at the gullery island for the rest of the season and prowled the gannetry. He scavenged and dozed while ninety sunrises exploded out of the east and the horizon was thinly dotted with gannets returning from sea hunts. From the cliffs where he stood the amphitheater of the sea east of the island was specked with the tiny white marks of a hundred birds, not the ten thousand of other years. Birds floated and waited for an answer to their hunger. Argen returned alone to the estuary as the gannetry broke up, the young puffins went out to sea, and the cormorants deserted their rocks.

The estuary was changed. Argen flew back and forth over the tidal sandflats, once so heavily populated with thousands of gulls but now coldly quiet. He flew past the silent estuary island. Its motionless pines thrust dark inverted images across the water.

The eelgrass meadows were dying. Instead of showing fluidly green under the water, they were yellowed and discolored and, in many places, the diseased grass was piled up on the shore in long lines, already gone scummy green with decay. As the fall matured, Argen, at low tides, became aware of growing expanses of sandy shingle and mud from which the eelgrass had gone entirely. He was led to these areas because the disappearance of the grass left many defenseless creatures out in the open. The fall gales savaged away at the dying grasses and Argen prowled among pools filled with small crabs, which, their eelgrass shelter gone, now sought sanctuary jammed half under stones.

While Argen prowled, the first of the brant geese arrived. They were querulous and hungry. Throughout their migration, they had found anticipated eelgrass pastures either gone or disappearing. This was causing the geese to bunch up, flock folding into flock, and sending them headlong to the south.

Argen heard the bulk of them arriving soon after midnight in a flock so huge that the sound of their wings was a solid roaring in mid-air. The brant passed over his sandbank and turned toward the estuary as their flight leaders picked out landmarks in the gloom which directed them toward the eelgrass. The sound of their wings died away and Argen resumed his dozing.

Before dawn he was awake and flying toward the estuary. As the first faint light lit the scene before him, he was confronted by the largest mass of birds he had ever seen. About one quarter of a million brant covered almost the whole estuary and created an undulating black, gray, and white mass which chuckled and gurgled and communicated its concern over the absence of the eelgrass. The tide was receding and the birds were trampling in thousands across the

muddy banks. Argen could see a gray-brown stain of dis-
placed sediment being carried away from the feeding
grounds of the brant.

The absence of the eelgrass at this crucial time was confusing. The brant waited at the estuary indecisively throughout that day and the next. Many ate other grasses or dug out
the nearly rotten stems of eelgrass from the mud. The brant
needed to feed heavily during their migration and the absence of the grass had a rapid effect. In the evening of the
second day, several tens of thousands of them took off and
headed south. The following day dawned clear and mild.
Argen found the estuary infested with a now ravenous flock
of brant. The birds' cries had changed; they were now more
urgent and penetrating. Small groups of birds seemed to be
attempting to escape the estuary and swung widely out to
sea, but then were drawn back. They settled and squawked.
The movements of birds intensified during the day. At evening, thousands more headed south.

On the fourth day, Argen sensed trouble among the brant.
Some seemed unwilling to fly and, when trying to take off
with their comrades, skittered low across the water. He saw
some brant standing alone on the mudflats and he could tell
by the strained attitudes of their bodies that they were in
distress. There was little flying on this gusty, gray, cold day
with fleeting bursts of sleet. Most of the brant stayed still and
quiet, muffled in their feathers as though dozing, awaiting the
next decisive impulse that would move them.

Argen had scarcely settled himself on the sandbank that
evening when the remaining brant took off. Their wings
roared, filled the estuary, and came to Argen like the sound
of a distant storm. The brant gathered over the estuary and
formed into columns, and soon they were streaming over

Argen's head in a thickening river of sound. As they flew, odd birds fell away as they became incapable of keeping up with the group. One landed near the dozing gulls, squawked with concern, and tried to take off. She failed and the gulls heard her beating wings and stamping feet receding across the shallow tidal waters that surrounded them. Then they heard only muted soft squawks as the bird stood motionless and impotent in the darkness while the sound of her comrades' wings swelled and then diminished.

The brant faded from memory. They would not be seen again at the estuary for many years. Bare mud glistened with footprints that covered every stretch of exposed land in futile searching. The gulls preyed on stricken brant for days.

The passing of the brant was merely an interlude that separated a hungry summer from a vicious winter. Argen was immersed in his memories of the cold times. Huddled in the snow, he faced a famine that had now become catastrophic, as the animal spirit became numbed or helpless and survival became a dull reflex. Only the strongest and most aggressive gulls survived. Argen was consumed by a need to subjugate his weaker comrades. He dug a large clam out of ice-encrusted sand, fought for it against a score of attackers, and only ended his fight for it in the dunes by thrashing one last gull, a youngster who, till that moment, had been sure that his strength and youth would prevail. He fled and left blood on the sand and his cries echoed his confusion at having his instinct denied by the cunning and resourcefulness of the old bird.

Waves became a counterpoint to the long scavenge. The cold sharpened and the sound of the waves became harsher. Argen sometimes slept on the ocean beach, where the noise of the sea was great. Spume dashed upward and froze, and pattered down on the sand. When he flexed his wings, he broke a sheath of ice that had formed on them.

The dark violence of the sea attracted him. It evoked a juvenile memory, of strength, exuberance, wild joy, and the conquest of the elemental force. Now that his experience was so great, he was sensitive to the difference between the present and the past. The thundering sea brought him images of his first offshore flight and, painfully, the sudden twist of wind that had put him into the surf, broken and helpless, seventeen years before. He listened and heard a seabird's cry far out to sea and then he dozed on the trembling sand.

As the winter wore on, its violence diminished and its cold grew less severe. Some nights were so calm that the chill moon burned a path to where he slept. Small waves whispered against the strand. Big waves hit the beach diagonally, pitched from the other side of the ocean by a storm which had churned among shearwaters breeding on distant islands, then among puffins and kittiwakes roaming the ocean. The waves grew and raced endlessly along the shoreline, breaking at only one point and speeding past Argen in a running roar of motion. One breaking wave dissolved into the dusk as another appeared and seemed to chase after it. The waves came incessantly, and Argen slept on and passed through the cold and the hunger and into a limbo of a new season at the shore.

CHAPTER 19

The Uncertain Season

A T I M E of dreaming enveloped the strand. Gulls sank into sleep and lined horizons and the edge of time with their silent presence. Water, waiting at a beach spotted with a thousand gulls, sparkled in the chill brilliance of midday. The light shifted and glittered at the estuary and the birds waited.

In his nineteenth year, Argen was drawing slowly away from the growing flocks of gulls who were pulled to the estuary by the end of the famine. The new gulls were all young, all aggressive, and they re-created the spirit of former years at the estuary. Argen felt more and more wary. He flew to the offshore fishing grounds in rough weather and was distressed so much during his return that he had to rest frequently. His crooked wing ached and he felt unaccountably weak. His old authority meant little to the new gulls.

As a reaction to this uncertainty, he became quarrelsome and short-tempered and ranged his territory with deliberately slow wing strokes, legs dangling below him. But he skirted conflict with other outwardly aggressive gulls. He was aware of weak or indecisive gulls, and when he saw a young gull catch a clam as he himself had done eighteen years before, he was thrown into action. The young bird, looking dubiously at his new find, had no time to experiment with it. He was knocked sprawling, and scrambled to his feet to see Argen flying away with the catch.

But aggressiveness did not reassure Argen now. A deep-rooted rage, reminiscent of the days of his prime, lurked unreleased in him. He was drawn in the direction of the young gulls; their sleek-bodied presences encouraged his rage. He walked around flocks of them, menaced them in their hunting, and received their humble acknowledgment. When one young gull was reluctant to defer to him, Argen's rage rose and he chased the youngster down the shore. Over the next few days, the two birds clashed several times on the feeding grounds, the young gull showing some desire to avoid a serious collision, the old gull driven to provoke it. Argen saw the young gull drop into the middle of the estuary and seize a fish. This triggered him into movement. He fell swiftly while the young gull was still trying to swallow. The collision bore the youngster deeply underwater. Argen heard him choking. The surface foamed around their struggle. As Argen ripped away feathers and tore flesh, he felt a triumphant release from his age. Strength seemed to flow into every muscle.

But the young gull swallowed the fish at last and met the next attack with savage force. Argen was seized by his upper mandible and twisted deeply under. He gasped water into his crop and lungs. His breast feathers were torn out. He felt his injured wing being pulled and pain shot agonizingly across his chest. He screamed, a cry muffled in icy water, and suddenly his anger was gone, replaced by an almost juvenile submissiveness.

He broke free and flapped weakly but was assailed from behind and driven underwater. He felt all his resources ebb. He surfaced, blind for a moment, and flinched in expectation of a new attack. But nothing happened. He shook the water off his head. Blood streaked his feathers. He looked around. The young gull had gone.

In the shock following the fight, Argen began a molt. He was dispirited. Something strange was happening to him during this molt. He was not dropping all his old feathers; many of the young feathers were not strong enough to force out the old. Worse, the molt persisted, with all its attendant malaise, throughout the summer, and killed his breeding urge. He ignored the gulls who were coming into sexual condition and hunted alone. Old feathers stuck out at angles from his body and irritated him as they whistled and vibrated in flight. Eventually he ripped most of them out. In the fall, the molt resumed; his feathers seemed alien and ill-fitting and he had no feeling of restoration. The molt dragged on. He passed through the winter, a tattered and ragged parody of his old self. This spurred him, during this unaccountably mild and misty season, to yank angrily at his plumage in an effort to transform it into its former gleaming sleekness.

When spring came, he did not mate at the estuary. The gulls gathered, clamorous and excited, but he stood detached, wanting to be involved but feeling no impulse. When flocks began leaving for the offshore island, he watched them closely and yearned for the intense spirit of comradeship and competition that possessed them. He raised his wings, but did not, could not, fly with them.

Only a chance encounter, days later, when the snow-patched shore was expanding its somberly bare substance in preparation for spring's flush of green, aroused Argen from his indifference. A very old female gull, a stranger at the estuary and unmated, approached him as he stood dozing alone on the tidal flats. She stood near him for half a morning, then, slowly, as though repeating a half-forgotten rite, she began circling him in the familiar importuning action. He watched her and felt a reaction growing inside him, faint and distant, but perceptibly a reaction. Eventually the two old birds flew together.

Under the stimulus of the female's presence, Argen cried out from the center of the estuary and drew his mate up from the estuary island and led her down toward the open sea. The two birds flew silently, absorbed in their mutual purpose. Argen was relaxed at this familiar re-enactment, while the female was eagerly aware of new sights unrolling, the estuary widening, curving strands of mud and sand sweeping away, hummocky islands appearing and fleeing underneath, and the sea an eye, opening wide beyond sheltering sandbars.

The gullery island seemed huge. Argen led his mate along the western cliffs, deeply shadowed from the morning sun, and still chilled by the passage of night. Water clicked on rocks and Argen cried *Kaa*, and the cry echoed back emptily, *Kaa—kaa—kaa*, and was gone. In his desire to delay the moment when he would confront the gullery, Argen was irresistibly impelled to act. There was no escape from the gullery. He flared his tail and rose sharply and was caught in an uprush of air and the broad, flat top of the island burst into sight in an uproar of images.

The two birds held themselves motionless in the wind and watched the hordes of gulls straggling away through stunted scrub and angular spruce branches, sweeping plateaus of nascent grassland and shrub. This was only the second time in his life that Argen had been a latecomer to the gullery and he was flooded by recollections of his juvenile year, when he had sought to join the gullery and had been rebuffed.

Now there was a haunting echo of this memory. A hostile emanation from the ground affected both gulls, and the female, disturbed by this, cried out. But Argen overcame his fear of the hostility. He flew toward the center of the gullery, to the knoll, to his territory. It was occupied. He hovered, watching the young gull who stood on the crown of the knoll. Argen waited for the rush of rage that would send him to attack the intruder. But the rage did not materialize. Cautiously, he let himself down and landed on one side of the knoll. His mate remained in the air, watching.

The ensuing day was a horror, a nightmare. The young gull attacked Argen and easily drove him off the territory. Immediately two other gulls were on him and drove him into the eager beak of another gull. He rebounded into a cluster of angry birds, drawn by the commotion, who were relentlessly hostile to the intruder. His mate hovered above the screaming confusion, still uncertain, having no territorial pride and no stimulus to join Argen in his desperate fight. He, on the other hand, knew only that he must fight and assert his need for territory, *his* territory, but the powerful animation of aggression simply did not come. He was now the victim. Harder, younger personalities subjugated him. By late afternoon, he had, after a score of skirmishes, retreats, attacks, beatings, and bluffings, found himself standing on the site of his first nesting place, sixteen years before. His mate was now with him, still watchful, though not as involved as he was in the lure of territory.

Argen looked down over the cliffs and saw murres speeding away from their cliffside roosts and preened his disheveled feathers. He flew with his mate in overcast and in moonlight to other islands and found solitary gulls, whose nests they raided together. The two old birds pillaged eggs in a small ternery on a rocky island. Their mating produced one egg. They stood at the edge of the gullery and watched the dynamic life around them. They were outsiders and they understood this; and they were by nature not a part of the community spirit of the excited young gullery birds.

Through all this period, Argen was troubled and restless. He stood in a dead spruce overlooking the nesting territory and the sea, but he did not perceive events with the incisive clarity of previous years. The movement of the gulls was vaguely menacing to him as he sought, through his simple senses, to establish the intentions of these aggressive, powerful youngsters. His egg hatched and he ranged wider in search of food.

All the distances around the gullery were noticeably greater. The island was much longer than it had been and the formerly exhilarating east wind was now very strong and cold. Argen found himself turning away from it while other gulls, beaks agape, hurled themselves madly into its force and disappeared over the eastern cliffs and out to the magnetic sea. As his view of the world and his physical appearance changed, so did his demeanor. His eyes, warmed by age, experience, and knowledge, now took on an odd expression of doubt. His physical stance was no longer forthright, but slightly hesitant.

He spent hours preening futilely at his ragged plumage, and such was his absorption that a day passed before he sensed the absence of his mate. He stood very still at the nesting site while the gawky youngster importuned him. He felt the immensity of oceanic distance on all sides. The horizon shone a line of fire into his eyes. He called for his mate, but she could not answer him. He turned toward other gulls, but they ignored his cracked cries of inquiry.

He immediately felt the impulse to fly to the mainland. But then he heard the cry of the nestling and a surge of stronger emotion stopped him. He fed the youngster and, for the rest of the season, torn between the urge to desert the youngster and the urge to feed him, he hunted and brought him safely to wing.

The tension of coping alone with this task exhausted him. The days merged into one another without definite form. Suddenly it was fall; he had no memory of the fate of his nestling or of returning to the estuary. Multitudes of birds clotted the burnished water of the flooding tidelands in the estuary. Suddenly it was cold; he was recoiling from the chill impact of water filtering through his thinning feathers. He flew ashore and worked hard to restore the formerly impenetrable layer of interlocking feathers which made his body warm and waterproof. He worked for hours to fluff the feathers around a wet spot on his body. But they did not respond well. Suddenly it was truly cold; he flew into wispy mists and the sound of winds in the dead reeds of the marsh sent shivers over his skin. He had no memory of landing alone on an ice-rimmed sandbar, but he was there and looking at a nearby beach where a thousand sleeping herring gulls whitened the ground.

Thick snow kissed his eyes and the estuary became whitely rounded into winter form. He faced into the wind and shivered. His feathers were fluffed to insulate him but he could not remember such cold. He flew to a midstream sandbank and settled to doze but soon began to shiver again. He flew to the shore and sought shelter in the lee of some rocks, but the cold seeped into his bones. He flew to the estuary island

and settled under the cliffs where a weak sun was trapped between sand and rock, but he felt alarmed by the overhanging proximity of the cliffs. Eventually he found warmth in the dunes. The day was icily cold, but a trickle of heat from the sun was trapped among the mountains of sand. He flew along a high sandbank which towered up beside a frozen fresh-water lake and settled on the slope of the lee side.

From over the peaked crest of the sandbank, he could hear the sough of surf striking the ocean beach. As he dozed, other gulls joined him. The heat oozed into them and they closed their eyes against the bright reflection of the sun from the lake's white ice. Most of the birds around Argen were old, though few were more than half his age, and all were refugees. Some had recently been shaken by accidents or attacks that had nearly destroyed them. Some were experiencing the ebbing of spirit which would soon kill them. Some were juveniles, huddled among the adults in silent, wary acknowledgment of their fears of the unknown.

The winter passed in a series of episodes in which Argen's memory of events was confused and vague. He flew with careful deliberation to the estuary but did not recall returning to the dunes. He ate very little. He remembered a long moment of tugging at the carcass of an old stranded fish while time stopped. Some days impinged painfully, filled with agonies of staying active and warm.

A lucid moment: He skulked among roaring trees during a storm and then was forced, shivering, from his refuge into the streaming air, where, he found, he was warmer flying than resting. The storm ended in the middle of a wingbeat. His next memory was dozing comfortably on a beach, the sea air warm and the sun bright.

In the next moment of clarity, wind was scouring away

the sand in the dunes; he looked toward the sea and saw a long dune smoking all along its summit. The dunes were moving. Dusty sand silently enveloped his legs. The wind increased and larger sand grains took to the air, pattered against his plumage, fell, kicked up other grains, which leaped aloft. A sibilant rush of movement caressed his paddles.

Spring came suddenly, a rush of passion, a thrust of wet snow. White clouds raced across the midday sun; the tide had turned but Argen lacked the energy to move. He yawned and shook himself and through half-lidded eyes watched dry dead seaweed rolling along a sand valley. The husked body of a small crab danced past. Crushed and splintered shells glistened. Ten thousand seasons lived in the sands. Argen roused himself and the dunes fell away and thickening green vegetation spread to his left. The estuary appeared finally. He let himself down with relief at the fringe of its screaming chorus.

Argen slept in the inertial grip of age. His mate of two years before, who had disappeared in the middle of the nesting season, had remated and was incubating two eggs at the gullery. One of his male youngsters died on the beach of an inshore island after being injured by a sportive falcon. The warmth spread and the sea quieted. A female sand wasp whined past Argen's ear and dug deeply into the sand. A sparrow's eggs hatched in a dunes bush and Argen heard the youngsters peeping. He dozed and dreamed.

A summer wind puffed at his ear. In the far north, one of his female youngsters was eaten by a wolffish. Another youngster, born five years before, looked down at three nestlings squirming under her belly. The heat became stifling. Argen glided along the ocean beach. The wasp laid a single egg at the end of her tunnel. She brought drugged flies and laid them round the egg. She came out of the sand, spread the spoil of her digging, and flew away. One of Argen's youngsters, one of his twelve surviving male progeny, crept into a crevice at the gullery island and died. A female nestling he had raised six years before broke a wing in a collision with a puffin. The sibilant cries of the nestling sparrows did not arouse Argen from his sleep. His desire to live was subordinate to his need to sleep.

He descended into an abyss of dreams and black horizons looming at the fringe of awareness. A driving northeast wind sent spume drifting and tugged at a whitely rippled sea. Argen awoke and it was not a dream. The gullery prepared for a storm. Gannets, murres, puffins, and cormorants came in from the sea and crouched on bare rocks. The wind blew on a rising tide. Argen finally acknowledged it and shook himself out of sleep. The sparrow settled on her youngsters. The sand hissed, blew in drifts, rustled into leaves of bushes, and ran, pattering, across Argen's disheveled plumage.

From out of the east, black as night, came hissing breakers and angular jabs of lightning which froze the tumultuous shore into momentary spasms of calm. The sand rose in clouds, built into drifts, and the sparrow fled her nest and her youngsters were drowned in sand. Argen was thin and tense. Glittering lightning hissed overhead and with a strangled cry he was carried away at high speed. Roaring trees fled under him; the dunes disappeared in their own murk. He was once again in battle with his environment, one moment at tree height, the next pelted by spray from an invisible body of water. The wind tossed him obliquely and lifted his tail and tipped him toward earth. He rode in fright across a dark land he did not know, toward a place for which he had no instinct.

But behind the terror was exhilaration, produced by blood

speeding through veins, heart pumping fiercely, eyes keen for danger, muscles tense, so that in a few moments he was transformed; vigorous resistance sustained him. The enormity of the storm enveloped him. He was nothing, but he was everything. He was Argen, the gull, alone and undefeated, and he was surviving.

CHAPTER · 20

In the Mist

A DENSE mist pushed against the cliffs and Argen's need to reach the gullery became urgent. He wanted to fly, but his body would not obey. He strained outward and the invisible sea sighed. As he looked, the rocks blurred and shifted confusingly and his sense of balance veered wildly and he fell back on his tail, wings asprawl. Flying seemed impossible and he saw no end to the abyss before him.

The flight through the mist had exhausted him. His crooked wing was sore. Blood pumped through it in a blur of pain; he could feel his heart surging violently. For a moment, caught in the uproar of his senses, he was back again in the middle of the storm that had driven him out of the dunes. The estuary had rocked into view ahead of him, a smoky white arena of driven spume. He had careered wildly over huddled groups of gulls sheltering among rocks and behind sandbanks, and then had been enveloped in spume at the estuary. His unexpected rejuvenation had made him scream, his calls lost in the deep-throated hiss of the wind. In the middle of the estuary, the red-cliffed island had loomed up suddenly and he had seen a group of gulls standing in the lee of a low tidal dune. He had dropped down, his wings twisted, and landed. His exhilarating rage and energy persisted; without pause, he walked among the birds and attacked. They scattered in astonishment. Two, who raised their wings in protest against the attack, had been swept away by the wind and sent sprawling across the sand. Argen had walked the full length of the sheltering birds, old feathers sticking out at all angles from his body, every line of his carriage expressive of arrogance, his desire to fight, his supremacy. The other gulls, beset by more comprehensible problems, yielded to him with alacrity, and he had walked back along their disordered ranks, menacing and pecking.

This re-creation of angry strength had propelled him into a new life at the estuary, and in later days he had ranged among the gulls with such waspish caprice that he was deferred to everywhere. He would land among a group of gulls and they would leap away to give him space. In one long moment of quiet, he had looked around him and felt the old power almost recaptured. In this resurgent mood, he had suffered his first loss of balance. He had been flying over the empty island of terns, brilliantly lit by an orange sun, when suddenly he sideslipped and fell, his crooked right wing bent upright, his left wing jabbing uselessly at the uprushing air. A weakness in the gut seized him. He fell without fear. As the water rushed up to him, he felt anger at his helplessness and with the rage came strength. His crooked wing came down against the air, overcame its pressure, and with a sudden jerk, he was flying a wingbeat above the water.

This loss of balance had disturbed him. Early one morning, after a cool night of heavy dew, he had looked out toward the hazy horizon and had seen an eagle flying inshore. The shape of the bird was unmistakable and it was bearing down on the gulls around Argen, all placidly unaware of the danger. He had screamed out his supreme danger call and flailed into the air. Instantly the gulls rose with multi-voiced screams and in a second the sandbank was empty. But as they milled around, no danger could be seen anywhere. Argen looked for the eagle but could not see it. He settled back on the bank and stood uncomfortably. But the vision came again. Once more the gulls rose in panic in response to his agonized call. This time, when the danger did not materialize, the gulls settled back on the sandbank quickly and Argen was left alone in the air, wheeling back and forth. Finally, when the vision came to him a third time, he rose alone. The other gulls remained in hunched attitudes of dreaming and ignored him.

During the next few days his discomfort had grown into a welter of delusions and attacks of imbalance. His wariness and nervousness had at last driven him to wanton aggression; in one fight with a juvenile gull, he had nearly killed the youngster, who fled, spattered with blood from wounds around his eyes. But behind him Argen had been left with senses reeling, exhausted, baffled. He looked at the estuary, not with any rage or confidence, but with chilling fear in his gut. All he had known had slipped beyond comprehension. The days passed in a blur of confusion, cries, fights, delusions, till finally his afflicted senses urged him to escape.

Everything led back to the nest and to his mother, to the time when he had been safe, with his parents at his wing to dispel fear and make him glow with warmth. He must return. The memory had suddenly become so sharp and clear that it all seemed to have happened yesterday. He had taken off at dawn and headed for the offshore island. He had kept flying even though he had run into thick mist midway down the estuary. The mist, and his ebbing strength, had eventually frustrated him and brought him to this ledge on the cliffs, from where, he knew, the gullery lay not far distant. But, looking into the mist, the image of the gullery was dying.

A falcon came out of a yellow sky and Argen fled toward the water. It was night and the groaning cry of a black-backed gull alerted the other gulls, but to what? Fear. Argen was scrabbling for a foothold on an ice mountain and fear was all around him, though there was no cry of danger, no sound at all except the rustle of his feathers and the scraping of his feet. The murres were bolting for the sea and the hissing roar of their voices was deafening, and auks swam lithely underwater and shot themselves up on rocks. The long blue distances of a strange land became visible and banks of mist closed in like death and cries were muffled and doubt was a twist in the throat. It was spring and sharp puffs of wind from an electric horizon sent the gulls blossoming up-ward and Argen rose above all of them and there, clearly visible and anticipated, was the gullery island, and he felt its pull.

It was night, and terror came with a wind loaded with ice and sand grains and it tugged at the gulls and one of them panicked and with a cry was swept away. The gullery was a great hive of life stretching out all around Argen. But then it was almost empty, a husk of life on a lonely island. The gannets were flying against the sun again and that was famil-iar. Argen's mate was brightly fixed on a sparkling sea and gulls alighted on the water as far as vision reached. The run of fish was enormous, greater than anything in the gulls' ex-perience, and the cries of expectation echoed under hot clouds. A gull disappeared underwater, and her cry hung, like pain. The rays of the sun slanted across the estuary. It was summer, and a gull was struck violently and fell, leaving a cloud of feathers hovering. It was fall, the sea now quiet, mist stealing among spruces, water purling, a gull dying in the shallows, the sun sinking.

The ducks landed in the estuary, black against the reddening sun. Herons pumped along slowly at the fringe of the marsh. Knots rose so thickly that Argen skirted them. The swallows clotted like flies against the cliffs. Images of the strand ran headlong, retained for no more than a moment. Puffins roared out of the mist and a straggle of fulmars chuckled loudly. Shellfish fell and burst and crabs watched warily and the murmur of millions of voices was the sound of time and of the earth.

In the confusion of images, the uproar of the estuary was a background, gulls black against sunsets, gulls twisting in mid-air, gulls clashing beaks, flailing wings, the sea alive with shrimp and hysteria in the air; suddenly, quiet and sleep. The shore stretched out; old gulls stood in the dunes, waiting. Sandpipers hissed past. Argen shook his head weakly and heard water dripping onto the rocks. The mist was as thick as ever.

He did not notice the slight brightening of the air as the mist began to clear. His eyes looked but scarcely saw. He stood up. The movement was a convulsive reaction of legs that had always lifted him to life. He moved forward. He was conscious of his need to fly, to return to the island, to be in the familiar place and in the safe dreaming time. He pitched forward, but not in flight. His wings did not open and he disappeared into the mist.

In this way, the sea finally received Argen, the herring gull.

A NOTE ON THE TYPE

❖❖❖❖❖❖❖❖❖

THIS BOOK *is set in* Electra, *a Linotype face designed by* W. A. DWIGGINS. *This face cannot be classified as either modern or old-style. It is not based on any historical model, nor does it echo any particular period or style. It avoids the extreme contrasts between thick and thin elements that mark most modern faces, and attempts to give a feeling of fluidity, power, and speed.*

Composed, printed, and bound by
The Haddon Craftsmen, Scranton, Pa.
Typography and binding design based on
originals by W. A. Dwiggins